HIGH RESOLUTION
GAS CHROMATOGRAPHY

THIRD EDITION

Editor
K. J. Hyver

Guest Author
P. Sandra

ii

LIST OF CONTRIBUTORS

Karen J. Hyver, Ph.D.
Hewlett-Packard, Avondale Division

Richard C. Gearhart, Ph.D.
Hewlett-Packard, Avondale Division

Paul Goodley, Ph.D.
Hewlett-Packard, Scientific Instruments Division

Roger Leibrand, Ph.D.
Hewlett-Packard, Scientific Instruments Division

Beverly Newton
Hewlett-Packard, Avondale Division

Richard J. Phillips, Ph.D.
Hewlett-Packard, Avondale Division

Winfred J. Sanders, Ph.D.
Hewlett-Packard, Avondale Division

Patrick Sandra, Ph.D.
Laboratory of Organic Chemistry
State University of Gent
Gent, Belgium

Edward B. Smith
Hewlett-Packard, Waltham Division

W. Dale Snyder, Ph.D.
Hewlett-Packard, Avondale Division

Michael Wilson
Hewlett-Packard, Avondale Division

ACKNOWLEDGEMENTS

This book is a tribute to the collective talents and technical expertise of the Hewlett-Packard Analytical Instruments Group; however, it is appropriate to acknowledge the contributions of several individuals.

My thanks to the advisory committee of Ray Dandeneau, Beverly Newton, and Winfred Sanders for the insight and assistance in the definition, content, and focus of this work. I also wish to thank the contributing authors for the commitment of their time and talents to this project, and Ed Smith, Fred Rowland, and John DeGood for their help in electronic data transmission.

My special thanks to Don Gagnon, Sarah Goetz, Cindy Haigh, Laurie Lee, Fred Reese, and Belinda Woodard for their talents on the graphics design and format; to technical editor, Beverly Bruns, for her assistance in editing and reviewing this book; and, finally, to Leonard and Nicholas.

Because of these efforts, this third edition of High Resolution Gas Chromatography has come to fruition. My sincerest gratitude to all those involved.

Karen Hyver

TABLE OF CONTENTS

INTRODUCTION

The separation science of gas-liquid chromatography may be defined as the partitioning of a component between two phases, with the gas phase in motion relative to the stationary liquid. In classical gas chromatography, the components of the sample are transported by the mobile phase through a column packed with solid support particles coated with the stationary phase. High resolution, or capillary, gas chromatography employs an open-tubular column with a stationary phase film on the inner wall. This type of column, introduced by M.J.E. Golay in 1957, offers a significant increase in separation capability in comparison to conventional packed columns, thus the term *high resolution* gas chromatography.

Traditionally, the scope of capillary gas chromatography has been for the separation of the following:

- Complex mixtures

- Components closely related chemically and physically

- Mixtures consisting of a wide breadth of compounds

However, capillary chromatography, using fragile glass open-tubular columns and more sophisticated instrumentation, was not considered a "practical" technique.

The perception of high resolution chromatography has changed dramatically since the introduction of flexible fused silica as a capillary column tubing material in 1979 by Dandeneau and coworkers at Hewlett-Packard (1). The inherent strength and flexibility of fused silica makes it easier to use and less fragile than delicate glass capillary columns. In addition, fused silica provides a more inert surface for improved capillary performance and less adsorption of active components.

In 1983, at the Second International Symposium on Capillary Chromatography in Tarrytown, NY, Hewlett-Packard was responsible for another significant advance in open tubular gas chromatography with the first commercial introduction of large-diameter fused-silica columns as an alternative to packed columns. This achievement has changed the *scope* of capillary chromatography for the analysis of volatile compounds and less complex mixtures. Incorporating the advantages of fused silica with packed column instrumentation, has made open tubular gas chromatography using larger diameter columns more amenable to routine usage (2,3).

The third edition of "High Resolution Gas Chromatography" will focus exclusively on fused-silica open tubular columns and other advances in column technology and instrumentation which have been responsible for the tremendous growth of high resolution chromatography since the publication of the second edition.

References

1. Dandeneau, R. D., and E. H. Zerenner. 1979. *HRC & CC* 2:351–356.

2. Ryder, B. L., J. Phillips, L. L. Plotczyk and M. Redstone. March 1984. *"Flexible Fused Silica – The Packed Column Alternative???", presented at The Pittsburgh Conference and Exhibition, Atlantic City, NJ.*

3. Larson, P., and B. Newton. February 1986. *HP Technical Paper No. 115* Publication No. 43-5954-7555.

CHAPTER 1. THEORY

K. J. Hyver

The critical step in developing a method for gas chromatography is determining the resolution required to effect the desired separation. Chromatographic resolution, R, is calculated according to Equation 1.

$$R = \frac{2(t_{R,j} - t_{R,i})}{W_{b,j} + W_{b,i}} \qquad \text{[Eq. 1]}$$

where

t_R is the retention time of components i and j

W_b is the peak width at the baseline

The ability of the chromatographic system to separate the "critical pair" is not only dependent upon their absolute retention times, but also the sharpness of their respective peaks (that is, the separation efficiency of the column).

Similar resolution can be achieved in both low- and high-efficiency chromatographic systems, as illustrated in Figure 1-1. Resolution is a complex interplay of the following chromatographic parameters: efficiency, selectivity, and retention. According to Equation 2:

$$R = \sqrt{\frac{n}{4}} \left(\frac{\alpha - 1}{\alpha}\right) \left(\frac{k}{k+1}\right) \qquad \text{[Eq. 2]}$$

where

n = the column efficiency expressed as the theoretical plate number

α = the selectivity factor

k = the solute partition ratio

In the case of the lower efficiency packed column illustrated in Figure 1-1, selectivity is the most significant factor contributing to resolution. Thus, the need for a wide variety of stationary phases in packed column gas chromatography. Using a highly efficient capillary or open tubular column, the resolution of complex mixtures can be achieved using a few preferred stationary phases. This chapter discusses the concepts of efficiency, selectivity, and retention as applied to high resolution gas chromatography and the interplay of these parameters in optimizing separation.*

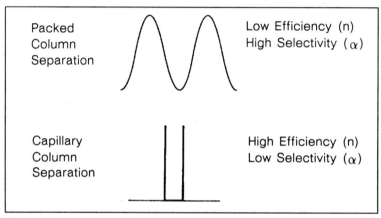

Figure 1-1. Comparison of equivalent resolution in a packed and capillary gas chromatography system.

Chromatographic Retention

The separation of individual components of a sample is achieved according to how each is uniquely retained by the chromatographic column. The time necessary for a component to elute from the column is termed the absolute retention time, t_R, and is measured at the peak maximum. During the chromatographic process, the component is partitioned

*Symbols and nomenclature used in this chapter are described in Appendix I.

between the mobile and stationary phases. The time spent in the mobile phase, t_m, is constant for all components of the mixture. Commonly called the column "dead time" or "hold-up time," t_m can be easily estimated from the retention time of a component unretained by the column, such as methane; however, mathematical dead time measurements have been shown to be more accurate (1,2).

The actual time that a component spends in the stationary phase can be calculated by the difference between the absolute retention time and t_m. The calculation for this value, termed the adjusted retention time, t_R', is shown in Equation 3.

$$t_R' = t_R - t_m \qquad \text{[Eq. 3]}$$

The relationships of t_R, t_m, and t_R' are illustrated in Figure 1-2.

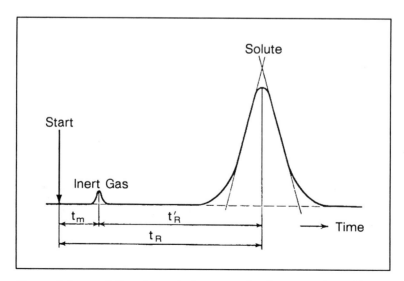

Figure 1-2. Relationship between absolute and adjusted retention time.

The solute partitioning between the two phases in a chromatographic column can be described as a dynamic equilibrium expressed by the partition coefficient, K_D, as shown in Equation 4.

$$K_D = \frac{C_{i,s}}{C_{i,m}}$$ [Eq. 4]

where

$C_{i,s}$ = concentration of component i in the stationary phase

$C_{i,m}$ = concentration of component i in the mobile phase

The partition coefficient has thermodynamic significance and is specific for a given component with respect to column temperature.

The partition ratio, k, is a measure of the molar distribution of the component between the liquid and gas phases. It is experimentally calculated from the ratio of the time the component spent in the stationary phase relative to the time spent in the gas phase.

$$k = \frac{n_{i,s}}{n_{i,m}} = \frac{t_R'}{t_m}$$ [Eq. 5]

where

$n_{i,s}$ = # moles of component i in the stationary phase

$n_{i,m}$ = # moles of component i in the mobile phase

The partition ratio is related to K_D by the phase ratio, β.

$$K_D = k\beta$$ [Eq. 6]

The phase ratio is the column volume occupied by the gas (or mobile) phase (V_m) relative to that volume occupied by the stationary liquid phase (V_s).

$$\beta = \frac{V_m}{V_s} \qquad \text{[Eq. 7]}$$

For a wall-coated open tubular (WCOT) column of internal radius, r, the phase ratio is inversely related to the stationary phase film thickness, d_f.

$$\beta = \frac{r}{2d_f} \qquad \text{[Eq. 8]}$$

Typical values of β for capillary columns range from 50 to 500, with the larger values indicating a thinner film.

In gas chromatography, a uniform expression of retention data is accomplished through the Kovats' Retention Index System (3). Kovats' retention indices normalize instrument variables, such as flow rate, so that retention data can be effectively compared for different chromatographic systems. It becomes the basis for component identification by chromatography. Retention index as a measure for qualitative analysis is discussed in Chapter 6.

The isothermal retention index, I_a^s, describes the retention of component "a" on stationary phase "s" as a hypothetical n-alkane. This is calculated according to the following equation based on the adjusted retention times of two hydrocarbons that bracket the component of interest.

$$I_a^s = 100N + 100n \left(\frac{\log t'_{R,\,a} - \log t'_{R,\,N}}{\log t'_{R,\,(N+n)} - \log t'_{R,\,N}} \right) \qquad \text{[Eq. 9]}$$

where

N   is the carbon number of the smaller n-alkane

n   is the difference in carbon number between the two alkanes

A thorough review of the retention index system is presented by Budahegyi *et al.* (4). The prediction of temperature-programmed retention indices calculated from isothermal data is described by Curvers *et al.* (5,6).

Separation Efficiency

Separation efficiency is a measure of the broadening of the solute plug as it travels the length of the column. It is defined in terms of the solute retention time and the standard deviation of the chromatographic peak. Assuming a Gaussian peak shape, column efficiency, termed the theoretical plate number, n, can be calculated from Equation 10.

$$n = \left(\frac{t_R}{\sigma}\right)^2$$ [Eq. 10]

The standard deviation of the peak (σ) can be estimated from its width as shown in Figure 1-3.

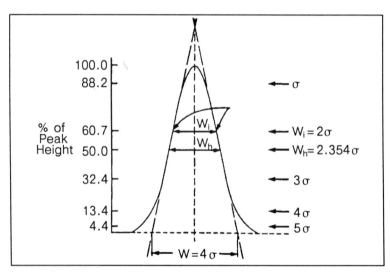

Figure 1-3. Peak width measured at different peak heights and σ of the Gaussian peak.

Accordingly, column efficiency can be expressed in terms of peak width at half height (W_h) or at the baseline (W_b) as follows:

$$n = 5.545 \left(\frac{t_R}{W_h} \right)^2 \qquad \text{[Eq. 11]}$$

$$n = 16 \left(\frac{t_R}{W_b} \right)^2 \qquad \text{[Eq. 12]}$$

Since peak width is generally measured at half height, the more common convention for the measurement of efficiency is Equation 11. Column efficiency is often normalized to column length (L), i.e., the number of theoretical plates per meter (n/L).

The efficiency of a column can also be expressed as the relationship of the height equivalent to a theoretical plate, h, or HETP. This is a measure of the column length in millimeters occupied by one theoretical plate and is an inverse relationship to n.

$$h = \frac{L}{n} \qquad \text{[Eq. 13]}$$

Thus, columns of high efficiency or large values of n will have small values for h.

Since the actual separating ability of a column is related to the amount of time the component spends in the liquid phase, efficiency has also been expressed in terms of the adjusted retention time (t'_R). This measure of column efficiency, the number of effective theoretical plates, is designated by N.

$$N = 5.545 \left(\frac{t'_R}{W_h} \right)^2 \qquad \text{[Eq. 14]}$$

The effective plate number is related to the theoretical plate number by the partition ratio.

$$N = n \left(\frac{k}{k+1} \right)^2 \qquad \text{[Eq. 15]}$$

Likewise, the inverse relation, the height equivalent to an effective theoretical plate (H or HEETP) is given by

$$H = \frac{L}{N} \qquad \text{[Eq. 16]}$$

HETP is used as the basic expression for theories which describe the influence of chromatographic parameters on column efficiency. The fundamental equation describing column chromatographic performance is the van Deemter Equation. This equation describes efficiency as a function of the average linear velocity of the mobile phase, $\bar{\mu}$. The abbreviated form of the classical van Deemter Equation is expressed as follows:

$$h = A + \frac{B}{\bar{\mu}} + C\bar{\mu} \qquad \text{[Eq. 17]}$$

where

A   is the term describing eddy diffusion, and accounts for multiflow paths of the mobile phase through eddies in the column

B   is the longitudinal diffusion term

C   is the resistance to mass transfer term

For open tubular columns that contain no support packing, the A term is nonexistent, thus reducing the van Deemter Equation to a form commonly referred to as the Golay Equation (7).

$$h = \frac{B}{\bar{\mu}} + C\bar{\mu} \qquad \text{[Eq. 18]}$$

In the Golay Equation, the longitudinal diffusion term, B, is given by the equation

$$B = 2D_m \qquad \text{[Eq. 19]}$$

where

D_m is the diffusion coefficient of the component in the mobile phase

This gas-phase diffusion coefficient can be predicted from the molecular weights and molecular diffusion volumes of the component and the carrier gas (8). Longitudinal diffusion is ever present, and acts to broaden the solute peak the longer the component stays in the column. Resistance to mass transfer is a function of the partition ratio, k, and describes the diffusion of a component into and out of the stationary liquid phase. Thus, the C term has two contributions.

$$C = C_m + C_s \qquad \text{[Eq. 20]}$$

Resistance to mass transfer in the mobile phase, C_m, is given by the equation

$$C_m = \frac{r^2}{D_m} \left(\frac{1 + 6k + 11 k^2}{24(1+k)^2} \right) \qquad \text{[Eq. 21]}$$

The resistance to mass transfer from the stationary phase, C_s, is determined from Equation 22.

$$C_s = \frac{d_f}{D_s} \left(\frac{2k^2}{4(1+k)^2} \right) \qquad \text{[Eq. 22]}$$

where

D_s is the diffusion coefficient of the component in the stationary liquid phase

For capillary columns of relatively thin film, C_s can be ignored.

Thus, separation efficiency is highly dependent upon column dimensions, as well as the physical properties of the solute and of the mobile and stationary liquid phases.

For WCOT columns, the minimum theoretical plate-height equivalent theoretically attainable (h_{min}) is given by:

$$h_{min} = r \sqrt{\frac{1 + 6k + 11k^2}{3(1+k)^2}} \qquad \text{[Eq. 23]}$$

This is the theoretical column efficiency obtained for perfect stationary phase coating under ideal conditions. The coating efficiency, or UTE (utilization of theoretical efficiency), expressed in terms of percentage is a measure of the comparison of the actual column efficiency to that theoretically predicted from Equation 23.

In capillary chromatography, another measure of column efficiency which is widely used is the separation number or Trennzahl (TZ). The Trennzahl, calculated according to Equation 24, is defined as the resolution of two consecutive members of a homologous series differing by one methylene unit.

$$TZ = \left(\frac{t_{R,\ (N+1)} - t_{R,\ N}}{W_{h,\ (N+1)} + W_{h,\ N}} \right) - 1 \qquad \text{[Eq. 24]}$$

The Trennzahl is related to resolution (R) by Equation 25.

$$TZ = \left(\frac{R}{1.177}\right) - 1 \qquad \textbf{[Eq. 25]}$$

Practically, the separation number is a measure of the number of peaks that could be separated between the two consecutive homologues, or the effective peak number. The calculation of Trennzahl is illustrated in Figure 1-4. The separation number for the capillary column calculated from the C_{12} and C_{13} alkanes is more than three times greater in comparison to that for the packed column. That is, the capillary column is capable of resolving 21 peaks between C_{12} and C_{13}; the packed column less than six. An advantage of the Trennzahl over other efficiency measures is its applicability to temperature-programmed separations. The TZ also has useful predictive value in its relation to the Kovats' Retention Index System (Equation 9). Assuming TZ is calculated from homologous n-alkanes:

$$TZ = \left(\frac{100}{\Delta I}\right) - 1 \qquad \textbf{[Eq. 26]}$$

Therefore, if the Kovats' retention indices (RI) are known for a critical pair, the separation number required to resolve them can be determined by applying the relationship in Equation 26. For example, to separate two components with a Kovats' RI of 1270 and 1274, respectively, ($\Delta I = 4$), a Trennzhal of 24 would be required. Thus, the capillary column operated under conditions in Figure 1-4 would not completely resolve this critical pair.

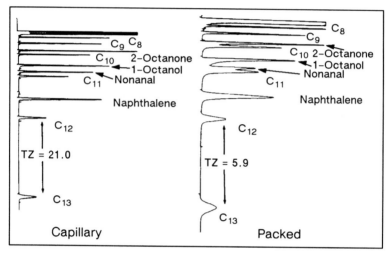

Figure 1-4.   Separation number calculated for a capillary and a
packed column. Capillary: 10 m x 0.25 mm coated
with methylsilicone. Helium, 35 cm/s. Packed:
1.2 m x 2 mm coated with 3% OV-101 on 100/200
Chromasorb W-HP. Helium 30 ml/min.

Selectivity

Selectivity refers to the selective physicochemical interactions
between the solutes and the chromatographic system. In gas
chromatography, selectivity is determined by the nature of the
stationary phase. The types of stationary phases for use in gas
chromatography have been reviewed in the literature
(9–11). Stationary phase selectivity is commonly expressed in
terms of the relative retention of a critical pair of sample
components, α.

$$\alpha = \frac{t'_{R,\,j}}{t'_{R,\,i}} \qquad\qquad \textbf{[Eq. 27]}$$

where

$$t'_{R,j} > t'_{R,i}$$

A value for the selectivity factor, α, greater than unity indicates
that separation can be achieved.

Solute-stationary phase interactions may include a mixture of nonpolar dispersive and specific polar interactions, such as dipolar interactions and hydrogen bonding. The terms "polar" and "nonpolar" have been commonly used to describe stationary phase selectivity; however, the synonymous use of polarity and selectivity is not accurate. Polarity is merely one component of selectivity resulting from stationary phase interactions involving polar moieties of the solutes. Selectivity is used to describe the result of a complex interplay of interactions between the solutes and the stationary phase.

A system to characterize stationary liquid phase selectivity has been established by McReynolds (12). The scale is based on the summation of the differences of the Kovats' retention indices of five probes (benzene, n-butanol, 2-pentanone, nitropropane, and pyridine) on the stationary phase of interest relative to squalane. The characterization of over 200 stationary liquid phases by McReynolds established a "polarity" scale which pointed out the similarities of many of the stationary phases used on packed columns. To simplify the redundancy of liquid phase offerings, a list of preferred stationary phases was suggested (13).

According to Stark et al. (11), the basic stationary phases used for coating fused silica WCOT columns are methylsilicones (OV-1, SE-33), phenylmethylsilicones (SE-54, OV-17), cyanopropylmethyl silicones (OV-225, OV-275), trifluoropropylmethylsilicones (OV-210), and polyethylene glycols (Carbowax 20M). For the majority of high resolution separations, these stationary phases provide more than adequate performance.

Columns with specialized selectivity can be obtained through selectivity tuning. This can be accomplished in one of three ways as illustrated in Figure 1-5:

- Tailor-made stationary phases
- Mixed-phase columns
- Serially coupled columns of different stationary phases

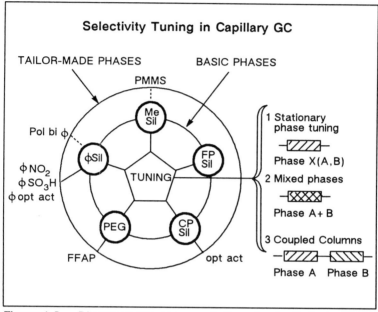

Figure 1-5.   Diagrammatic representation of selectivity tuning of stationary phases in capillary GC. Reproduced with permission from Reference 15 (HRC & CC, Huethig Verlag). Abbreviations are given in Appendix II.

Tailor-made phases can be specially synthesized from the basic stationary phases and designed to perform specific separations. For example, polyethylene glycol (PEG) can be acid-terminated to form a free fatty acid phase (FFAP) for the separation of nonesterified fatty acids.

Specialty columns can be prepared to optimize resolution for specified or standard analyses by mixing relative amounts of two distinct stationary phases. In cases where the two phases are immiscible, a copolymer can be synthesized which contains the relative percentages of the selective functional groups of the two individual stationary phases. Once the separation on the individual phases is established, the actual composition of the mixture or the copolymer can be determined by applying the techniques of window diagramming (14). Examples of this type of selectivity tuning include the environmental specialty columns used for the analysis of volatiles. A complete discussion of the concept of selectivity tuning is given by Sandra and coworkers (15).

Practical Implications of Chromatographic Theory

Resolution and the time required for a separation are functions of several interrelated column and operational parameters. Major factors that influence separation are column internal diameter, column length, the type of stationary phase and its film thickness, type of carrier gas, carrier gas velocity, and column temperature. A complete understanding of how these parameters affect the chromatographic analysis is an invaluable aid in column selection and methods development. The first four of these parameters are characteristic of the column and need to be considered when choosing the best column for the analysis. The three remaining parameters are operational and can be changed easily.

The effect of the type of carrier gas on chromatographic resolution is illustrated in Figure 1-6. It can be best described by examining the mobile phase diffusion terms of the Golay Equation. The efficiency curves for nitrogen, helium, and hydrogen obtained on a 0.25 mm id WCOT column are shown in Figure 1-7. It should be noted that the greatest efficiency (minimum HETP) can be obtained using nitrogen. However, this minimum value occurs over a narrow range of low carrier gas linear velocities with efficiency sharply decreasing proportionate to increasing average linear velocity. With nitrogen as the carrier gas, speed must be sacrificed for optimal resolution. Therefore, N_2 is not commonly used in capillary GC. On the other hand, because of the lower viscosity of hydrogen, changes in carrier gas velocity will not influence column resolution significantly. The minimum of the efficiency curve for hydrogen occurs over a much broader

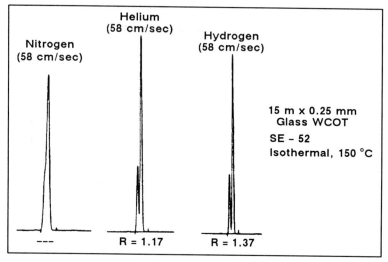

Figure 1-6. Effect of carrier gas on the resolution of n-heptadecane and pristane.

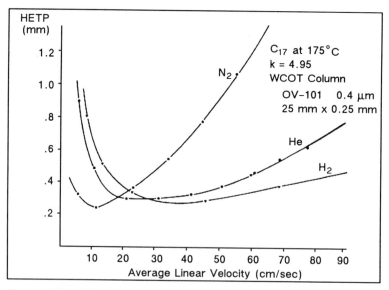

Figure 1-7. Efficiency curves for a 25 m x 0.25 mm id WCOT column with 0.4 μm of OV-101.

range and at higher linear velocities. This "flatness" in the efficiency curve makes hydrogen the carrier gas of choice for high resolution gas chromatography.

Column temperature has a dramatic effect on separation. The logarithm of the partition ratio, k, is inversely proportional to the temperature. The lower the column temperature, the greater is the partition ratio, thus increasing the time that the component spends in the stationary liquid phase (Equation 5). Increased retention in the stationary liquid phase allows greater advantage to be taken of the selective properties of that stationary phase. However, the chromatographer should be aware that selectivity can change with temperature and result in peak reversals.

Changes in the stationary phase film thickness or column internal diameter will change the phase ratio, β, and greatly influence the partition ratio (see Equation 8). An increase in film thickness (or decrease in the phase ratio) will result in an increase in the partition ratio and, therefore, increase component retention and resolution. This is illustrated in an analysis of gasoline shown in Figure 1-8. Increased resolution, however, is accompanied by a dramatic increase in analysis time.

Analysis time, measured as the retention time of the last eluting peak, is given by the equation:

$$t_{R,x} = \frac{L}{\bar{\mu}} (1 + k_x) \qquad \text{[Eq. 28]}$$

where

k_x is the partition ratio of the last eluting peak

Reducing column length will decrease the analysis time at the expense of resolution. This may not be a severe handicap since most chromatographic separations are performed on capillary columns with more than adequate resolution.

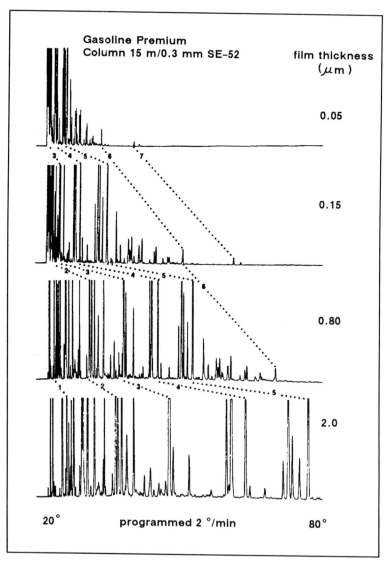

Figure 1-8. Analysis of gasoline on columns with varying stationary phase film thickness. (K. Grob and G. Grob, *HRC & CC*, 2 (1979) 109, reprinted with permission)

For fast capillary gas chromatography without significant loss in resolution, column internal diameter should be reduced to 0.1 mm or less. Several papers in the recent literature (16-18) discuss the advantages and limitations of narrow bore WCOT columns for high-speed capillary GC. Within the limits of current instrumentation, 100 μm id columns of 5 to 10 m in length can be operated with minor modifications.

The most serious limitation of reduced-diameter columns is the associated decrease in sample capacity. Capacity is the ability of a column to tolerate high concentrations of solutes. Degradation of chromatographic performance is seen when the column capacity is exceeded. This situation is commonly referred to as "overload" and is indicated by peak broadening and asymmetry as shown in Figure 1-9 for a 100 μm id fused silica capillary column coated with a 0.17 μm film of cross-linked 5% phenylmethyl silicone.

Sample capacity is related to the film thickness and phase ratio as illustrated in Figure 1-10. Figure 1-10 shows the log plots of the film thickness versus the phase ratio and the column capacity relative to a 250 μm id column with a 1 μm film. Curves are shown for the commonly used commercial FSWCOT column internal diameters between 50 μm to 530 μm. By extrapolating the appropriate curve for the desired column diameter from the film thickness, both the phase ratio of the column and its relative sample capacity can be determined. For example, a 3 μm film on a 530 μm id column (β of 45) has 5 1/2 times the sample capacity of the 250 μm id column. Thus, the chromatographer can easily estimate the change in sample capacity in association with change in internal diameter for a given phase ratio or film thickness.

Understanding the elements of efficiency, speed, capacity, and resolution is helpful when optimizing a chromatographic separation. Interrelationships between column and operational parameters must be considered. Small-diameter ($\leq$0.2 mm id) columns offer high-efficiency and high resolution advantages at the expense of sample capacity. Low

resolution, wide bore fused silica WCOT columns (≥0.53 mm
id) have much higher sample capacities and are best for
simple, packed column-like separations. Figure 1-11 gives a
comparison of the types of fused-silica capillary columns
available and their associated range in efficiency and sample
capacity. Further considerations in column selection are
discussed in Chapter 2. However, Figure 1-11 may be used as
a simple guide in selecting general column type when
developing an analytical method using capillary gas
chromatography.

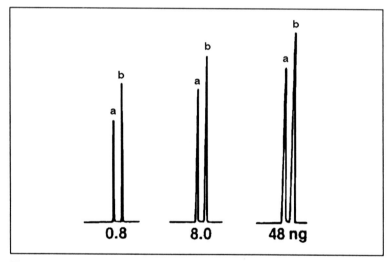

Figure 1-9. Peak shape of (a) dodecanol and (b) n-pentadecane
with increasing amounts of sample on the column.
Column: 10 m x 0.10 mm x 0.17 μm cross-linked
FSWCOT. Sample capacity is reached at 8 ng/com-
ponent.

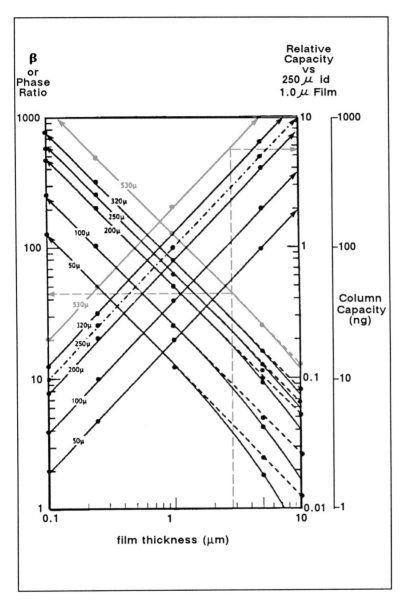

Figure 1-10. Log relationship between film thickness, phase ratio, and capacity. (Courtesy of D. C. Villalanti, Shell Development Company, Houston, TX)

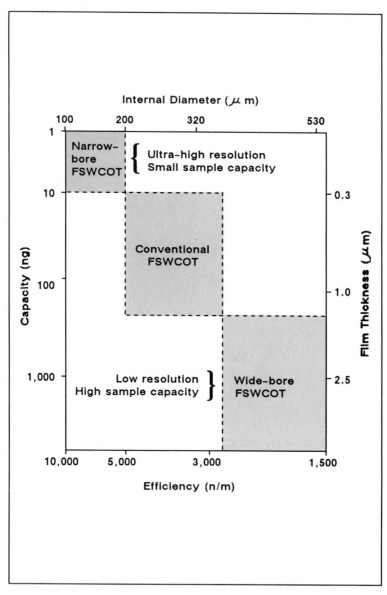

Figure 1-11. Comparison of chromatographic performance parameters for the range of available fused silica WCOT columns.

References

1. Wainwright, M. S., J. K. Haken, and D. Srisukh. 1979. *J Chromatogr* 179:160-166.

2. Parcher, J. F. and D. M. Johnson. 1980. *J Chromatogr Sci* 18:267-272.

3. Kovats, E. 1966. *Advances in Chromatography, J.C. Giddings and R.A. Keller, Eds., Marcel Dekke, New York* 1:229-247.

4. Budahegyi, M. V., E. R. Lombosi, T. S. Lombosi, S. Y. Meszaros, Sz. Nyiredy, G. Tarjan, I. Timar, and J. M. Takacs. 1983. *J Chromatogr* 271:213-307.

5. Curvers J., J. Rijks, C. Cramers, K. Knauss, and P. Larson. 1985. *HRC & CC* 8:607-610.

6. *Ibid,* 611-618.

7. Golay, M. J. E. 1958. *Gas Chromatography, V.J. Coates, H.J. Noebels and I.S. Fargerson, Eds., Academic Press, New York* pp. 1-13.

8. Fuller, E. N., P. D. Schettler, and J. C. Giddings. 1966. *Ind Eng Chem* 58(5):19-27.

9. Blomberg, L. 1982. *HRC & CC* 5:520-533.

10. Haken, J. K. 1984. *J Chromatogr* 300:1-77.

11. Stark, T. J., P. A. Larson, and R. D. Dandeneau. 1983. *J Chromatogr* 279:31-40.

12. McReynolds, W. O..1970. *J Chromatogr Sci* 8:685-691.

13. Hawkes, S., D. Grossman, A. Hartkopf, T. Isenhour, J. Leary, J. Parcher, S. Wold, and J. Yancey. 1975. *J Chromatogr Sci.* 13:115-117.

14. Laub, R. J., and J. H. Purnell. 1976. *Anal Chem* 48:799-803.

15. Sandra, P., F. David, M. Proot, G. Diricks, M. Verstappe, and M. Verzele. 1985. *HRC & CC* 8:782-798.

16. van, Es A., J. Janssen, R. Bally, C. Cramers, and J. Rijks. 1987. *HRC & CC* 10:273–279.

17. Sandra, P. 1987. *LC–GC* 5:236–246.

18. Hyver, K. J., and R. J. Phillips. 1987. *J Chromatogr* 399:33–46.

CHAPTER 2. THE COLUMN

B. Newton

The column is often termed the "heart of the chromatographic system." A thorough understanding of the column will simplify many aspects of performing modern capillary gas chromatography. This chapter provides a practical overview of the columns used in high resolution gas chromatography. Because of their overwhelming use in contemporary capillary GC, only fused-silica capillary columns are discussed.

Glass capillary gas chromatography was already a well-known, though relatively unpopular, technique in the late 1970s when Hewlett-Packard began research on capillary columns. Sparked by research in fiberoptic technology, the flexible fused-silica capillary column was developed. Further investigation by Ray Dandeneau *et al.* led to the introduction of the fused-silica capillary column at the 1979 Capillary Chromatography Symposium in Hindelang, West Germany (1). Fused silica was presented as "unexcelled by any material tested" and it "established a new chromatographic standard in inertness and ease of use due to its high flexibility."

The introduction of commercially available fused-silica capillary columns in late 1979 marked a major breakthrough for capillary gas chromatography. In 1979 less than 10% of gas chromatographs sold used capillary columns. Now, in 1989, more than 60% of all GCs manufactured are equipped with capillary capability. This number is expected to increase as further developments in capillary columns permit the analysis of both high-temperature compounds and highly volatile gases.

Fused-Silica Column Tubing Material

Manufacture of Capillary Tubing

A schematic diagram of a typical capillary drawing machine (2–4) is shown in Figure 2-1. The raw material is fed into a high-temperature furnace (~2000°C). The fused-silica capillary tubing is drawn out of the furnace while maintaining strict control over the internal and external diameters. The capillary tubing is coated with an outer protective layer. A variety of materials have been used, ranging from polyimide (by far the most commonly used) to gold. Examples are shown in Figure 2-2.

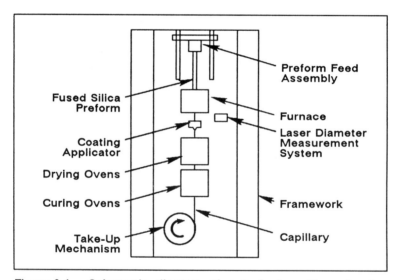

Fused Silica Preform

Coating Applicator

Drying Ovens

Curing Ovens

Take-Up Mechanism

Preform Feed Assembly

Furnace

Laser Diameter Measurement System

Framework

Capillary

Figure 2-1.   Schematic diagram of a typical capillary drawing machine.

Tubing and Tubing Strength

Although many glass materials may be drawn in such a way as to give flexibility and strength, only synthetic fused silica gives the necessary inertness needed to chromatograph difficult compounds such as drugs, pesticides, acids, and amines (5,6).

Quartz tubing is also commercially available; however, it contains a concentration of metal oxides that is too high for most uses in gas chromatography (7). Although synthetic fused-silica tubing is inert due to its low metal oxide content (<1 ppm), surface silanol groups are still present and do contribute to the residual activity of the column. Several techniques have been proposed in the literature to minimize or cover up these active sites (8–23). The process of minimizing the active sites is called deactivation.

Figure 2-2. Photograph of capillary tubing material with outer protective coatings of polyimide and aluminum.

Residual column activity is important to the chromatographer. Inertness varies greatly from one column to the next. Column performance tests may not be stringent enough to identify potential activity for the variety of sample components which can be introduced. (See Figure 2-3.)

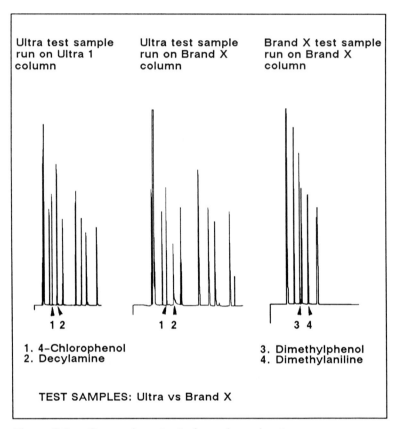

Figure 2-3. Comparison tests for column inertness.

Flexible capillary tubing is inherently straight; therefore, to install the tubing in a traditional gas chromatograph, it must be wound into a circle (usually requiring a frame to hold the tubing in place). The resultant stress on the tubing is dependent upon the diameter of the frame and the internal diameter of the tubing; see Figure 2-4. In a practical sense, the smaller the diameter of the column frame, the higher the stress and the higher the likelihood of a fracture occurring over time. Large internal-diameter tubing is especially susceptible to stress fractures. Tubing should be stress tested to minimize such fractures.

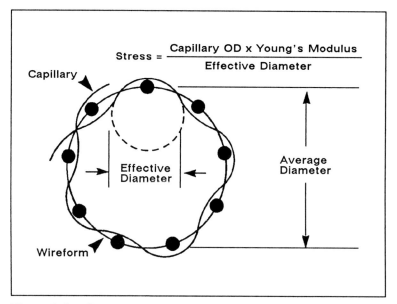

Figure 2-4.   Stress on the capillary tubing when wound on a wireform.

In addition to stress fractures, uncoated fused-silica capillary tubing is susceptible to moisture in the air (humidity). Water molecules attack the silicon-oxygen bonds forming silanol groups and open cracks which will propagate into a fracture over a fairly short period of time as shown in Figure 2-5. Protecting the silica from moisture and scratches is the main reason for the outer coating of either polyimide or some other equally resistant material.

Column Types

A good understanding of the use of capillary columns begins with an understanding of the terminology. Perhaps the most important terms to become familiar with are capacity, resolution, efficiency, and selectivity. The theory of capillary gas chromatography and its practical implications are discussed in Chapter 1. An understanding of these terms and their interrelationships will prove useful in selecting the appropriate column for the desired analysis.

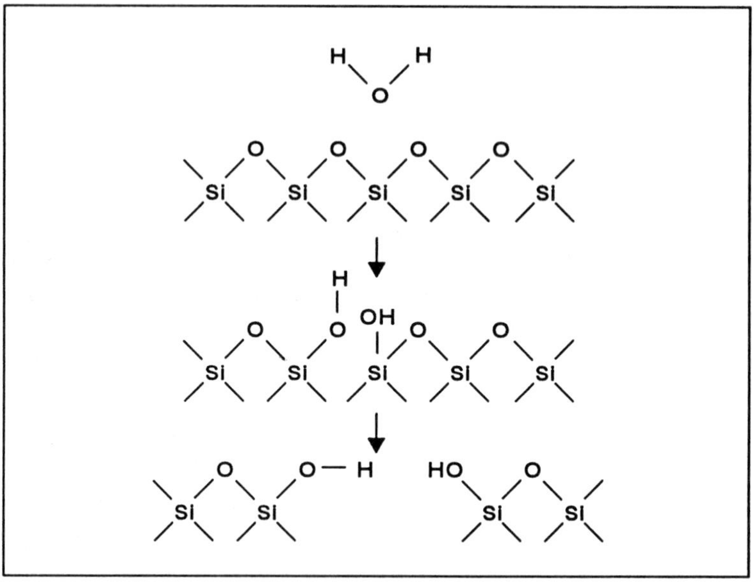

Figure 2-5.   Static fatigue of fused silica.

WCOT, PLOT, SCOT, and Micropacked

Wall-coated open tubular (WCOT) capillary columns are by far the most commonly used at this time. However, recent advances in porous layer open tubular (PLOT) columns may soon increase the popularity of this type of column.

Commercially available WCOT capillary columns are made of capillary tubing (0.05 mm to 0.53 mm internal diameter) with a film (0.1 μm to 8.0 μm) of stationary phase uniformly applied to the inside of the capillary wall; see Figure 2-6. The stationary phase is a polymer in the form of a viscous fluid (OV-225), a gum (OV-1, SE-30), or a solid (Carbowax 20M, Superox). These phases are dissolved in solvents and coated onto the inside of the capillary tube using a variety of techniques. Dynamic or static coating techniques are the most popular, with ultradynamic or supercritical fluid techniques still under investigation (24–37). After coating, the stationary phase may be cross-linked and/or bonded.

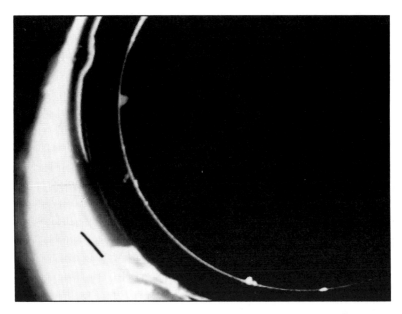

Figure 2-6.   Electron micrograph of a fused-silica wall-coated
open tubular column.

WCOT capillary columns offer high efficiency for the difficult separation of a large number of sample constituents. However, standard film thicknesses do not have a high sample capacity for concentrated samples and are not effective in separating very light molecular weight substances or inert gases at ambient temperatures.   Very thick film WCOT columns have been developed to overcome these limitations (38–40).   Other sample solutions available for increased capacity and better retention for volatile compounds include PLOT, SCOT, and micropacked capillary columns.

PLOT capillary columns are made of fused- silica tubing with an internal layer of an adsorbent material; see Figure 2-7.   To date, these materials have consisted of aluminum oxide/KCl, a molecular sieve, and porous polymers (similar in chemical composition to Porapak Q).   An excellent explanation of PLOT column manufacture, theory, and applications has been published by de Zeeuw and de Nijs (41,42). The disadvantages of these columns are:

- lower efficiency
- loss of inertness
- reproducibility/stability problems over time

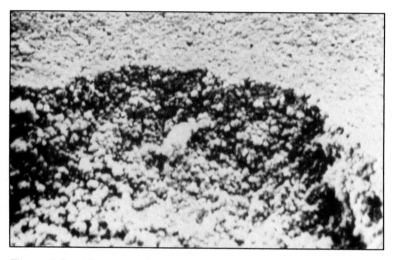

Figure 2-7.   Electron micrograph of the adsorbent used in PLOT columns. (Courtesy of Chrompack International, The Netherlands)

Support-coated open tubular (SCOT) capillary columns are of less interest in high resolution GC due to the inertness problems associated with the support material. In SCOT columns, the liquid phase is coated onto a support material adhered to the wall of the capillary. The main advantage of these columns for practical use is the possibility of a wider range of stationary phases on fused silica. Since most experts agree that only a limited number of phases are needed for high resolution GC, SCOT columns have yet to show much promise.

Micropacked capillary columns are columns with the internal diameter completely filled with a support material (43–46). Micropacked and SCOT capillary columns may be used increasingly in the future for certain specific applications; however, widespread use of these columns does not seem realistic at present.

Stationary Phases—Types (Cross-Linked vs. Bonded) and Stability

In general there are nine standard (most frequently used) liquid phases commercially available for WCOT columns today. In addition a wide variety of custom blended or "designer" phases is available from various manufacturers for specific applications (47–78). The standard phases and their relative chromatographic properties are listed in Table 2-1.

Table 2-1. Common Stationary Phase Coatings for Fused-Silica WCOT Columns.

Composition	Polarity	Applications	Phases with Similar McReynold's Constants	Temp Limits
1. 100% dimethyl polysiloxane (Gum)	Nonpolar	Phenols, Hydrocarbons, Amines, Sulfur Compounds, Pesticides, PCBs	OV–1, SE–30	– 60° C to 325° C
2. 100% dimethyl polysiloxane (Fluid)	Nonpolar	Amino Acid Derivatives, Essential Oils	OV–101, SP–2100	0° C to 280° C
3. 5% diphenyl 95% dimethyl polysiloxane	Nonpolar	Fatty Acids, Methyl Esters, Alkaloids, Drugs, Halogenated Compounds	SE–52, OV–23, SE–54	– 60° C to 325° C
4. 14% cyanopropyl phenyl polysiloxane	Intermediate	Drugs, Steroids, Pesticides	OV–1701	– 20 to 280 °C
5. 50% phenyl, 50% methyl, polysiloxane	Intermediate	Drugs, Steroids, Pesticides, Glycols	OV–17	60° C to 240 °C
6. 50% cyanopropylmethyl, 50% phenylmethyl polysiloxane	Intermediate	Fatty Acids, Methyl Esters, Alditol Acetates	OV–225	60° C to 240° C
7. 50% trifluoropropyl polysiloxane	Intermediate	Halogenated Compounds, + Aromatics	OV–210	45 °C to 240 °C
8. polyethylene glycol – TPA modified	Polar	Acids, Alcohols, Aldehydes Acrylates, Nitriles, Ketones	OV–351, SP–1000	60° C to 240° C
9. polyethylene glycol	Polar	Free Acids, Alcohols, Ethers, Essential Oils, Glycols, Solvents	Carbowax 20M	60° C to 220° C

Due to the relatively small number of available phases, and the large number of applications published over the last five years, phase selection can be a fairly simple matter. Because of the need for low-bleed phases that have adequate stability for coating onto fused silica surfaces, many phases used today are manufactured specifically by the column supplier. Although these manufactured phases may give excellent performance, low bleed, and high efficiency, there is one drawback. A column coated with a phase from one supplier may not give the same separation as an equivalent phase from another supplier. This becomes more obvious with the polar phases and can be further aggravated by the variety of manufacturing techniques used to produce the columns (79). The differences in these phases are most commonly manifested as varying degrees of inertness to certain classes of compounds (i.e., alcohols, acids, amines) and peak movement (i.e., retention time/index changes) (80), as illustrated in Figure 2-8.

Although the peak movement changes may be minor (5–10 RI units), this phenomenon can be disastrous to users trying to determine chemical identification by GC. This problem is widespread enough so that many GC methods now specify both the column type to be used and the manufacturer. Unfortunately, specifying the manufacturer still may not guarantee the reproducibility of the written method. The reason for this is the fact that the process and specifications used by the manufacturer will influence the reproducibility of the columns made. If a method is written using a "better-than-average" column from a manufacturer, a "worse-than-average" column from the same manufacturer may not do the separation needed.

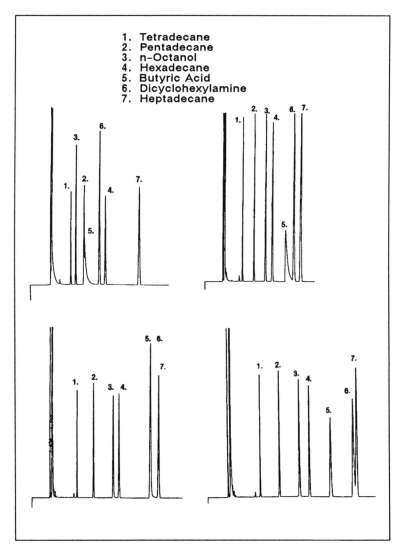

Figure 2-8. Comparison chromatograms of a test sample on four
cross-linked Carbowax 20M columns from four
commercial manufacturers.

As discussed, a custom or "designer" phase may often be developed by the column supplier for a specific application. In this case the phase may be a mixture of two or more standard phases, or it may be a phase specially synthesized to give specific desired qualities for a certain application. Since small changes in the chemical composition of a liquid phase can radically change the chromatographic separation obtained, all phases (designer and standard) need thorough characterization prior to use in chromatography. Presently used qualification techniques consist of:

Analytical Technique	Desired Information
Gel Permeation Chromatography	molecular weight distribution (81)
UV/VIS	phenyl content
Thermal Gravimetric Analysis	thermal stability of the phase
Infrared	presence of special functional groups (i.e., cyano)
NMR	location of chemical functionality within the phase molecule
GC-MS	functional group substitution (82)

An issue still under discussion with respect to stationary phases is the difference between cross-linked and bonded phases. What exactly are the benefits to be gained from these treatments? For most analyses, the stationary phase must be durable to solvent injections and thermally stable over a reasonable life of the column (83). Column stability after 100 on-column injections of a sample dissoved in methanol is compared in Figure 2-9. Column performance is virtually unchanged after 100 injections as evidenced by the retention time stability and peak symmetry. The quality of the column permits the integrity of an analysis to be maintained under stressful conditions.

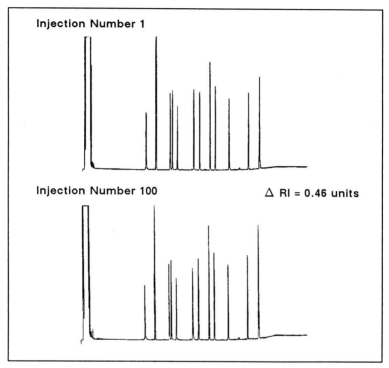

Figure 2-9. Comparison of column performance after 100 on-column injections of a sample dissolved in methanol.

To achieve this stable performance under high stress conditions, the stationary phase must be immobilized by cross-linking and/or bonding. Cross-linking refers to the reaction that causes individual stands of polymer phase to bond together forming a larger, more stable, macromolecular film. Bonding refers to the process of chemically attaching the stationary phase to the surface of the fused silica. To date, many papers have been written demonstrating the greater durability and temperature stability of cross-linked phases. Cross-linking (vulcanization, immobilization) of the stationary phase is achieved through the use of free radical initiators. Some of these initiators include peroxides (84–86), gamma radiation (88–94), ozone (87), and azo compounds (95). To produce quality reproducible columns, each of the free radical initiators requires an optimized process for its use. A typical cross-linking reaction is illustrated in Figure 2-10.

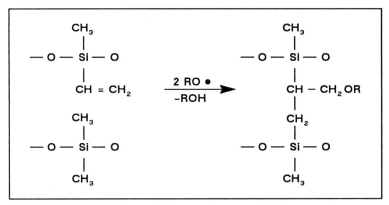

Figure 2-10. Typical mechanism of a cross-linking reaction.

Due to the difficulties of cross-linking the more polar phases, some manufacturers still offer both cross-linked and non-cross-linked phases. Since cross-linked columns can be rinsed with solvents for column regeneration, but the noncross-linked columns cannot be rinsed; users should be aware of the type of column purchased before trying to rinse them with solvents.

The phase-coating efficiency is listed as a percentage of what is theoretically possible. Usually values of 90–100% are achievable on the nonpolar silicone phases and values of 60–80% on the more polar phases. The percent coating efficiency is a measure of the uniformity with which the stationary phase has been applied onto the fused silica wall. A more uniform coating maximizes the total number of plates for a given column. Polar phases do not "wet" the surface of fused silica as well as nonpolar silicone phases and, therefore, do not produce as many total plates per length of column; see

Table 2-2. Since total column efficiency is also related to the id of the column, larger id columns can have very good coating efficiencies with much lower total plate counts.

Table 2-2.   Comparison of Average Efficiency by Phase and Internal Diameter (given in plates/meter and % coating efficiency).

	Methyl Silicone (nonpolar)	50% Phenyl (intermediate polarity)	Carbowax 20M (polar)
0.1 mm id	10,000/90%	------	------
0.2 mm id	4,500/90%	4,200/80%	4,000/70%
0.32 mm id	3,200/90%	3,000/80%	2,500/70%
0.53 mm id	1,500/75%	1,350/60%	1,300/60%

Some general information on phase stability at both high and low temperatures is given in Table 2-1. Because cross-linked phases are generally more stable, they can be heated or cooled over a broader temperature range than their noncross-linked counterparts. Column bleed at high temperatures is a function of thermal decomposition and contamination. Conditioning and cross-linking the standard phases available today decreases the amount of column bleed per unit time, but does not completely eliminate it. Therefore, to minimize column bleed at high temperatures, it is necessary to minimize the volume of the phase within the column. Hence, thin film columns (0.1 μm or less) are best suited for high-temperature work. Another limitation to high- temperature GC is the polyimide coating, which is stable for only a few days at continuous use above 380°C. This problem has recently been addressed with the introduction of aluminum-coated fused-silica columns (96–98). Some typical applications for these columns are shown in Figure 2-11.

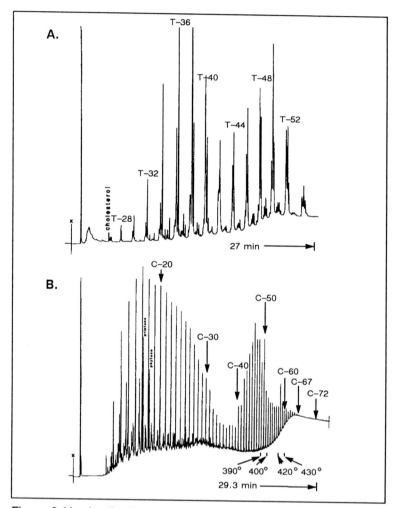

Figure 2-11. Applications of high-temperature GC using aluminum-coated fused silica columns. A. Triglycerides in butter. B. Canadian crude oil. (Courtesy of Quadrex Corporation, New Haven, CN).

Column Selection

The following are the most common methods used for column selection:

- Try a column that is handy
- Ask a colleague for advice
- Look for a similar application that has already been published

Although these are tried and true methods, they lack finesse in optimizing the chromatographic separation. In other words, the user may end up with an adequate method, but one which will be far from optimal for speed of analysis, separation, and/or column lifetime. Needless to say, all endeavors must begin somewhere and these methods are good enough to get started; however, these methods should not be the only criteria used. From this point, the chromatography should be analyzed and the following rules of thumb used to optimize the separation in the presence of the following problems.

Problem: No resolution (separation) of the desired components.

Solution: Select a longer column or one with a smaller inside diameter (id) to increase efficiency. When already working at the longest length and the smallest id, the only choice left is to change phases to adjust the selectivity of the separation.

Problem: Too much resolution. (The sign of inexperience!)

Solution: Select a shorter length, thinner film, or larger id column. More resolution than what is necessary is wasted. By not optimizing resolution, analysis times can be unnecessarily long. (Remember, a major advantage of fused-silica columns is that they can be cut to any desired length.)

Problem: Poor peak shape.

Solution: If the column has been installed properly and the instrument is well maintained, then poor peak shape can be attributed to any one or a combination of the following three possibilities:

    i. The sample component is incompatible with the phase. Try a different phase and remember that "like dissolves like". Therefore, use polar phases with polar sample components.

    ii. The column may not have been made with your needs in mind. Contact the supplier and review the specifications for that column with respect to your needs.

    iii. The sample may be too concentrated for the film thickness of the phase being used. Reduce the sample load on the column or go to a thicker film liquid phase.

Problem: Excessive column bleed at high temperature.

Solution: Change to a thinner film, cross-linked column.

It is important to select the optimum column for the separation by considering some of the following column characteristics:

- efficiency (plates/meter)
- k value (a measure of film thickness reproducibility)
- retention index values (measures of the chemical nature of the column)
- peak heights of base/acid (a measure of the inertness of the column)
- bleed (a measure of the temperature stability of the column)

With this information and some thought, chromatographers can confidently select the column best suited to meet the needs of their analyses.

Column Evaluation and Performance

Many column test samples have been suggested in the literature over the past 10 years (99–103). Two of the typical polarity blends used to test column performance are illustrated in Figure 2-12. Selected test samples are used to evaluate the column for a variety of performance needs such as inertness, retention index, efficiency, etc. (104). The result is an indication of the general quality of the column. Under these conditions, a stringent set of test compounds along with tight quality control specifications is desired.

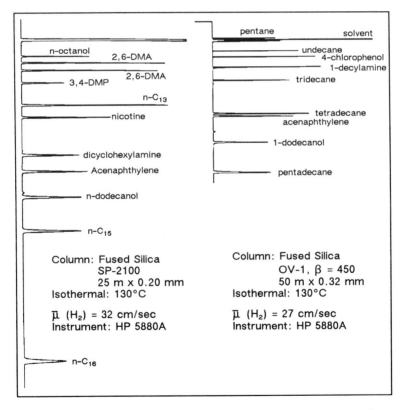

Figure 2-12. Typical column performance samples analyzed on fused silica WCOT columns.

However, testing conditions may have little or no bearing on column quality or lifetime as seen by the user. The user's samples may contain easier or more difficult compounds to chromatograph than those in the sample. Also, the user is interested in column performance over 100 to 2,000 injections. Therefore, the column test sample used by the manufacturer need not, and perhaps should not, be the same one used in the laboratory. The best situation would be a test sample created in the user's laboratory to give custom information most relevant to the chromatographic needs of that laboratory. This sample should contain pesticides if used in an environmental lab, drug compounds if used in a toxicology lab, and so on. Since few column manufacturers actually test their columns with a drug or pesticide, this "custom" test would give a more relevant indication of column performance to the user.

Once a relevant test sample is identified, the integrity of the sample must be maintained. Since most test samples are susceptible to decomposition, only fresh samples of known good condition should be used. A decomposed sample will give false indications of column performance. In addition, false indications of column performance can be obtained from poorly maintained chromatographic systems and/or incorrect column installation, as shown in Figure 2-13.

How to Monitor Column Performance

1. Select a relevant evaluation sample
2. Assure proper GC performance
3. Run evaluation sample periodically (weekly, monthly)
4. Collect data and plot over column life
   Efficiency or resolution
   Inertness measure (base/acid ratio)
   Retention index
   Bleed

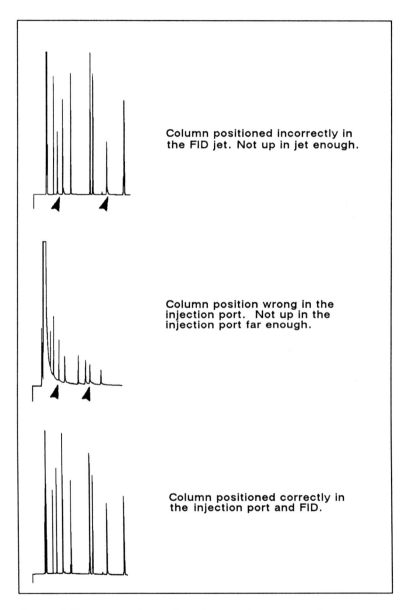

Column positioned incorrectly in
the FID jet. Not up in jet enough.

Column position wrong in the
injection port. Not up in the
injection port far enough.

Column positioned correctly in
the injection port and FID.

Figure 2-13. Comparison of system performance with proper and
improper installation.

Many of the everyday problems encountered in a chromatography laboratory can be eliminated when the lab maintains good quality control information (i.e., control charts) regarding its columns, samples, and chromatographic systems. A summary of the most important performance indicators is shown below.

Summary of Performance Indicators

EFFICIENCY

> **Effective theoretical plate count**
> **(isothermal)**

RESOLUTION

> **Separation number**
> **(temperature programmed)**

ACTIVITY

> **Peak symmetry measurements**
> **Peak height variation**
> **(e.g., base/acid ratio)**

COLUMN TO COLUMN REPRODUCIBILITY

> **Retention index variation**
> **k variation**

Column Conditioning, Maintenance, and Storage

A freshly deposited liquid phase will retain residual traces of solvents, along with lower molecular weight liquid phase fractions. These products progress through the column and emerge at the detector as "column bleed" to yield a baseline offset and extraneous peaks. Therefore, preconditioning of the column by the user may be necessary. In addition, periodic conditioning of older columns may be necessary due to the accumulation of nonvolatile material from the sample or impure carrier gas.

A degree of compromise is necessary when selecting the conditioning temperature. High conditioning temperatures achieve stable baselines more rapidly but shorten column lifetime. Lower conditioning temperatures may prolong column life, but longer conditioning time is needed to achieve stable baselines. Selection of the conditioning temperature should take into consideration the operating temperature of the GC and the temperature limits of the liquid phase. If the proposed analyses involve temperatures of under 200°C, then there is no reason to condition the column above 250°C. Overnight conditioning at normal flow rates and 220°C would be sufficient and more likely to prolong column life. It is recommended that the column be disconnected from the detector during conditioning to minimize condensation of the liquid phase materials and contaminants at the detector. Before heating above 50°C, new columns should be purged for five minutes with pure carrier gas at normal flow rates to remove any adsorbed oxygen. Carrier flow through the column should be confirmed before heating the column. Columns are destroyed quickly by exposure to high temperatures with no flow or with a very restricted flow of carrier gas. It is important to check the suggested temperature limit from the column supplier, since these limits do vary from one column manufacturer to the next.

When the liquid phase is disturbed, the column efficiency drops dramatically. Splitless and on-column injections of samples can often displace the liquid phase over the first one or two meters of the column. In this case, it is recommended that the defective section be removed; the shortened column may continue to be used. One or two meters taken off the column should not be detrimental to the total efficiency.

Poor carrier gas quality and incompatible samples can be detrimental to column lifetime as can oxidation (Figure 2-14) and overheating (Figure 2-15)(105). Silicone phases are resistant to water injections (Figure 2-16), but are affected adversely by acidic samples. Cross-linked or noncross-linked Carbowax 20M phases are easily oxidized by oxygen in the carrier gas and can have low lifetime when used in conjunction with aqueous samples. Some solvents, such as carbon disulfide and diethyl ether, may also have detrimental effects on the liquid phases.

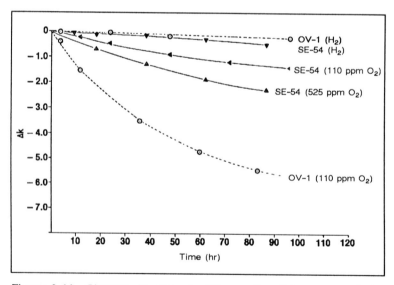

Figure 2-14. Change in the partition ratio (k) measured for pentadecane as a function of stress at 325°C.

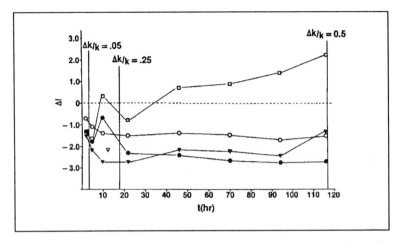

Figure 2-15. Effect of thermal stress at 400°C measured as the
change in retention index (ΔI) on SE-54 for
▼ acenaphthalene, ● n-decylamine, ○ n-dode-
canol, and □ 4-chlorophenol.

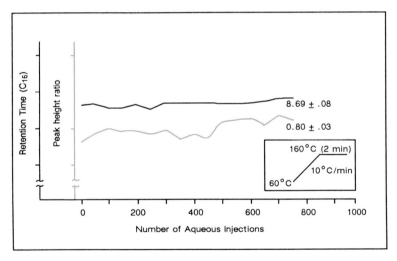

Figure 2-16. Effect of water injections (2 µl/injection) on retention
time and column inertness measured as the ratio of
peak heights of p-chlorophenol and n-decylamine for
a cross-linked methylsilicone column.

If the liquid phase is compromised by the accumulation of nonvolatile components in the sample matrix, column performance may be restored by:

i. Removing a meter or two of column from the injection port end.

ii. Turning the column around and reconditioning it overnight with flow.

iii. Rinsing the column (Figure 2-17). This is the most extreme measure. In general, only 50% of the columns rinsed can be regenerated. Therefore, complete loss of the column is possible with this method.

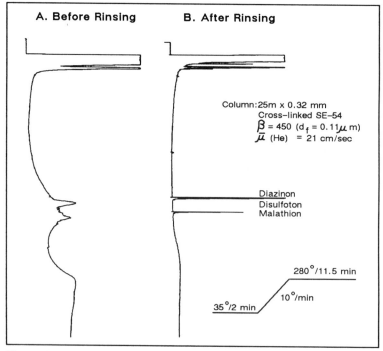

Figure 2-17. Effect on a pesticide analysis when rinsing the column. A) chromatogram of a pesticide extract after repeated on-column injections. B) chromatogram after rinsing the column with 9/1 methylene chloride: methanol.

Other restoration methods have been reported with varying results (106,107).

The column should also be safeguarded when not in use. There are two storage safeguards of greatest importance:

1. Store the column so it will not be scratched. If scratched, the stress to the column upon heating may be great enough to allow the column to break at the weak point.
2. Seal the column ends to protect the liquid phase against diffusing oxygen and contaminants.

When using fused-silica columns, remember that fused silica is a glass material and eye protection should be used.

Future Trends

At present, trends in fused-silica capillary column development include the use of:

1. Shorter columns with smaller internal diameters giving ultra-high column efficiency and speed. (108,109)
2. PLOT capillary columns for capillary gas-solid adsorption chromatography.
3. Higher temperature phases and exterior coatings for the fused silica tubing.
4. Mixed or "custom" phases for specific applications.

In many of these areas the future opportunities will be dependent on new modifications to the chromatography instrumentation available. These modifications could be as minor as higher temperature ovens or faster electronics, or they could be as extensive as design of an instrument that utilizes a "drop-in" column or the "column-on-a-chip" concept (110).

In conclusion, the use of fused-silica capillary columns can be challenging and rewarding given a working knowledge of their strengths and weaknesses. As in all aspects of science, nothing ventured, nothing gained.

References

1. Dandeneau, R. D., and E. H. Zerenner. 1979. *Proceedings of the Third International Symposium on Glass Capillary Chromatography* pp. 81–97. Hindelang.

2. Pretorius, V., and D. H. Desty. 1982. *Chromatographia* 15:569–574.

3. Ryder, B. L. 1983. *The Manufacture of Fused Silica Tubing with Exceptional Durability.* Pittsburgh Conference and Exposition.

4. Lipsky, S. R., W. J. McMurray, M. Hernandez, J. E. Purcell, and K. A. Billeb. 1980. *J Chromatogr Sci* 18:1–9.

5. Ogan, K. L., C. Reese, and R. P. W. Scott. 1982. *J Chromatogr Sci* 20:425–428.

6. Lipsky, S. R. 1983. *HRC & CC* 6:359–365.

7. Lipsky, S. R., and W. J. McMurray. 1981. *J Chromatogr* 217:3–17.

8. Stark, T. J., R. D. Dandeneau, and L. Mering. 1980. *The Role of the Deactivating Agent in the Preparation of Fused Silica Capillary Columns.* Pittsburgh Conference and Exposition.

9. Buijten, J., L. Blomberg, K. Markides, and T. Wannman. 1982. *J Chromatogr* 237:465–468.

10. Woolley, C. L., K. E. Markides, M. L. Lee and K. D. Bartle. 1986. *HRC & CC* 9:506–514.

11. Kong, R. C., C. L. Woolley, S. M. Fields, and M. L. Lee. 1984. *Chromatographia* 18:362–366.

12. Welsch T., and H. Frank. 1985. *HRC & CC* 8:709–714.

13. Markides, K. E., B. J. Tarbet, C. M. Schregenberger, J. S. Bradshaw, M. L. Lee, and K. D. Bartle. 1985. *HRC & CC* 8:741–747.

14. Rutten, G., J. de Haan, L. van de Ven, A. van de Ven, H. van Cruchten, and J. Rijks. 1985. *HRC & CC* 8:664–672.

15. Woolley, C. L., R. C. Kong, B. E. Richter, and M. L. Lee. 1984. *HRC & CC* 7:329–332.

16. Traitler, H. 1983. *HRC & CC* 6:60–63

17. Moseley, M. A., and E. D. Pellizzari. 1982. *HRC & CC* 5:472–475.

18. Pretorius, Victor, and D. H. Desty. 1981. *HRC & CC* 4:38–39.

19. Markides, K. E., B. J. Tarbet, C. L. Woolley, C. M. Schrengenberger, J. S. Bradshaw, M. L. Lee, and K. D. Bartle. 1985. *HRC & CC* 8:378–384.

20. Venema, A., and J. T. Sukkel. 1985. *HRC & CC* 8:705–708.

21. van de Ven, L. J. M., G. Rutten, J. A. Rijks, and J. W. de Haan.1986. *HRC & CC* 9:741–746.

22. Xu, B., and N. P. E. Vermeulen.1986. *HRC & CC* 9:679–682.

23. Blum, W. 1986. *HRC & CC* 9:120–121.

24. Redant, G., P. Sandra, and M. Verzele. 1982. *Chromatographia* 15:13–14.

25. Xu, B., and N. P. E. Vermeulen.1985. *HRC & CC* 8:181–185.

26. Xu, B., and N. P. E. Vermeulen. 1984. *Chromatographia* 18: 642–644.

27. Xu, B., and N. P. E. Vermeulen and J. A. M. Smit. 1986. *Chromatographia* 22:213–218.

28. Grob, K., G. Grob, and K. Grob Jr. 1981. *J Chromatogr* 211:243–246.

29. Grob, K., and G. Grob. 1981. *J Chromatogr* 213:211–221.

30. Grob, K., and G. Grob. 1982. *HRC & CC* 5:119–123.

31. Grob, K., and G. Grob. 1985. *HRC & CC* 8:856–857.

32. Janak, K., V. Kahle, and K. Tesarik. 1985. *HRC & CC* 8:843–847.

33. Kong, R. C., and M. L. Lee. 1983. *Chromatographia* 17:451–453.

34. Wannman, T., L. Blomberg, and S. Schmidt. 1985. *HRC & CC* 8:32–44.

35. Arrendale, R. F., R. F. Severson, and O. T. Chortyk. 1983. *HRC & CC* 6:436–439.

36. Kong, R. C., and M. L. Lee. 1983. *HRC & CC* 6:319–321.

37. Rohwer, E. R., V. Pretorius, and G. A. Hulse. 1985. *HRC & CC* 8:693–694.

38. Sandra, P., I. Temmerman, and M. Verstappe. 1983. *HRC & CC* 6:501–504.

39. Grob, K., and G. Grob. 1983. *HRC & CC* 6:133–139.

40. David, F., M. Proot, and P. Sandra. 1985. *HRC & CC* 8:551–557.

41. de Zeeuw, J., R. C. M. de Nijs, and L. T. Henrich. 1987. *J Chromatogr Sci* 25:71–83.

42. de Nijs, R. C. M. 1981. *HRC & CC* 4:612–615.

43. Malik, A., A. R. Jumaev, and V. G. Berezkin. 1986. *HRC & CC* 9:312–313.

44. Berezkin, V. G., A. Malik, and V. S. Gavrichev. 1983. *HRC & CC* 6:388–389.

45. Malik, A., V. G. Berezkin, and V. S. Gavrichev. 1984. *Chromatographia* 19:327–334.

46. Benecke, I., and G. Schomburg. 1985. *HRC & CC* 8:191–192.

47. Al-Thamir, W. K. 1985. *HRC & CC* 8:143.

48. McManemin, G. J., and W. Reuter. 1985. *HRC & CC* 8:80–81.

49. Grobler, A., and G. Balizs. 1981. *J Chromatogr Sci* 19:46–51.

50. Freeman, R.R., and D. Kukla. 1986. *J Chromatogr Sci* 24:392–395.

51. Buijten, J., L. Blomberg, K. Markides, and T. Wannman. 1982. *Chromatographia* 16:183–187.

52. Horka, M., V. Kahle, K. Janak, and K. Tesarik. 1986. *Chromatographia* 21:454–459.

53. Hinshaw Jr., J. V., and L. S. Ettre. 1986. *Chromatographia* 21: 561–572.

54. Hinshaw Jr., J. V., and L. S. Ettre. 1986. *Chromatographia* 21: 669–680.

55. Takeuchi, T., H. Kitamura, T. Spitzer, and D. Ishii. 1983. *HRC & CC* 6:666–668.

56. Farbrot, A., S. Folestad, and M. Larson. 1986. *HRC & CC* 9:117–119.

57. Ogden, M. W., and H. M. McNair. 1985. *HRC & CC* 8:816–823.

58. Mehran, M. F., W. J. Cooper, R. Lautamo, R. R. Freeman, and W. Jennings. 1985. *HRC & CC* 8:715–717.

59. Sandra, P., F. David, M. Proot, I. G. Diricks, M. Verstappe, and M. Verzele. 1985. *HRC & CC* 8:782–798.

60. Bradshaw, J. S., N. W. Adams, R. S. Johnson, B. J. Tarbet, C .M. Schregenberger, M. A. Pulsipher, M. B. Andrus, K. E. Markides, and M. L. Lee. 1985. *HRC & CC* 8:678–683.

61. K.E. Markides, H-C Chang, C.M. Schregenberger, B. J. Tarbet, J.S. Bradshaw and M.L. Lee. 1985. *HRC & CC* 8:516–520.

62. Rokushika, S., K.P. Naikwadi, A.L. Jadhav, and H. Hatano. 1985. *HRC & CC* 8:480-484.

63. Benecke, I., and G. Schomburg. 1985. *HRC & CC* 8:191-192.

64. Bradshaw, J. S., S. J. Crowley, C. W. Harper, and M. L. Lee. 1984. *HRC & CC* 7:89-92.

65. Kuei, J. C., J. I. Shelton, L. W. Castle, R. C. Kong, B. E. Richter, J. S. Bradshaw, and M. L. Lee. 1984. *HRC & CC* 7:13-18.

66. Abe, I., S. Kuramoto, and S. Musha. 1983. *HRC & CC* 6:366-370.

67. Vigh, Gy., J. Hlavay, Z. Varga-Puchony, and T. Welsch. 1982. *HRC & CC* 5:124-127.

68. Wright, B. W., P. A. Peaden, and M. L. Lee. 1982. *HRC & CC* 5:413-416.

69. Sandra, P., M. Van Roelenbosch, I. Temmerman, and M. Verzele. 1982. *Chromatographia* 16:63-68.

70. Ahnoff, M., and L. Johansson. 1984. *Chromatographia* 19:151-154.

71. Aerts, A., J. Rijks, A. Bemgard, and L. Blomberg. 1986. *HRC & CC* 9:49-56.

72. Lee, M. L., R. C. Kong, C. L. Woolley, and J. S. Bradshaw. 1984. *J Chromatogr Sci* 22:136-142.

73. Stark, T., P. A. Larson, and R. D. Dandeneau. 1983. *J Chromatogr* 279:31-40.

74. Schomburg, G., I. Benecke, and G. Severin. 1985. *HRC & CC* 8:391-394

75. Bemgard, A., L. Blomberg, M. Lymann, S. Claude, and R. Tabacchi. 1987. *HRC & CC* 10:302-318

76. Kuei, J. C., B. J. Tarber, W. P. Jackson, J. S. Bradshaw, K. E. Markides, and M. L. Lee. 1985. *Chromatographia* 20:25-30.

77. Pulsipher, M. A., R. S. Johnson, K. E. Markides, J. S. Bradshaw, and M. L. Lee. 1986. *J Chromatogr Sci* 24:383–391.

78. Matisova, E., D. Hudec, J. Garaj, G. Kraus, M. Schierhorn, and A. Isenberg. 1985. *Chromatographia* 20:601–608.

79. Jennings, W. G., R. H. Wohleb, and R. G. Jenkins. 1981. *Chromatographia* 14: 484–487.

80. Kramer, J. K. G., R. C. Fouchard, and K. J. Jenkins.1985. *J Chromatogr. Sci.* 23:54–56.

81. Vigh, Gy., A. Bartha, and J. Hlavay. 1981. *HRC & CC* 4:3–5.

82. Temmerman, I., P. Sandra, and M. Verzele. 1985. *HRC & CC* 8:513–515.

83. Pizzala, R. U., R. R. Freeman, and L. L. Plotczyk. 1983. *Hewlett-Packard Application Note 228-30* HP Pub No. 43-5953-1708.

84. Grob, K., and G. Grob. 1981. *HRC & CC* 4:491–494.

85. Martinez de la Gandara, V., J. Sanz, and Martinez-Castro. 1984. *HRC & CC*7:44–45.

86. Lipsky, S.R., and W.J. McMurray. 1982. *J Chromatogr* 239:61–69.

87. Chuang, C.H., H. Shanfield, and A. Zlatkis. 1987. *Chromatographia* 23:169–170.

88. Etler, O., and Gy. Vigh. 1984. *HRC & CC* 7:700–701.

89. Vigh, Gy., and O. Etler. 1984. *HRC & CC* 7:620–624.

90. Barry, E. F., G. E. Chabot, P.Ferioli, J. A. Hubball, and E. M. Rand. 1983. *HRC & CC* 6:300–305.

91. Hubball, J. A., P. R. DiMauro, E. F. Barry, E. A. Lyons, and W. A. George. 1984. *J Chromatogr Sci* 22:185–191.

92. Schomburg, G., H. Husmann, S. Ruthe, and M. Herraiz. 1982. *Chromatographia* 15:599–610.

93. Hubball, J. A., P. R. DiMauro, S. R. Smith, E. F. Barry. 1984. *J Chromatogr* 302:341–350.

94. Etler, O., and Gy. Vigh. 1985. *HRC & CC* 8:42–44.

95. Richter, B. E., J. C. Kuei, N. J. Park, S. J. Crowley, J. S. Bradshaw, and M. L. Lee. 1983. *HRC & CC* 6:371–374.

96. Lipsky, S. R., and M. L. Duffy. 1986. *HRC & CC* 9:376–382.

97. Lipsky, S. R., and M. L. Duffy. 1986. *LC-GC* 4:898–906.

98. Lipsky, S. R., and M. L. Duffy. 1986. *HRC & CC* 9:725–730.

99. Seferovic, W., J. V. Hinshaw Jr., and L. S. Ettre. 1986. *J Chromatogr Sci* 24: 374–382.

100. de Nijs, R. C. M., and R. P. M. Dooper. 1980. *HRC & CC* 3:583–584.

101. Freeman, R. R. 1983. *Hewlett-Packard Application Note AN228-36* HP Pub No. 43-5953-1747.

102. Grob Jr., K., G. Grob, and K. Grob.1978. *J Chromatogr* 156:1.

103. Temmerman, I., and P. Sandra. 1986. *HRC & CC* 9:117–119.

104. Moncur, J.G. 1982. *HRC & CC* 5:53–55.

105. Larson, P., T. Stark, R. Dandenau. 1981. Proceedings of the Fourth International Symposium on Capillary Chromatography. *Hindelang, R.E. Kaiser, Ed.* pp 727–750.

106. Schwarz, Meyer, and J. A. Klun. 1982. *HRC & CC* 5:380–381.

107. Ogden, M.W., and H.M. McNair. 1985. *HRC & CC* 8:326–331.

108. Proot, M., and P. Sandra. 1986. *HRC & CC* 9:618–623.

109. Farbrot, A., S. Folestad, and M. Larsson. 1986. *HRC & CC* 9:117–119.

110. Pacholec, Frank. 1986. *LC-GC* 4:432–441.

Additional Reading

Blomberg, L. G., and K. E. Markides. 1985. *HRC & CC* 8:632–650.

Blomberg, L. G. 1984. *HRC & CC* 7:232–241.

Ettre, L. S. 1985. *Anal Chem* 57:1419–1436.

Duffy, M. L. 1985. *Am Laboratory* 94–105.

Grob, K. 1987. *J Chromatogr* 398:391–392.

Hinshaw, J. 1988. *LC-GC* 6:24–29.

Tarbet, B. J., J. S. Bradshaw, K. E. Markides, B. A. Jones, and M. L. Lee. 1988. *LC-GC* 6:233–248.

CHAPTER 3. SAMPLE INTRODUCTION
P. Sandra

Introduction

"If the column is described as the heart of chromatography, then sample introduction may, with some justification, be referred to as the Achilles heel." This citation of Pretorius in 1983 (1) clearly illustrates that sample introduction is of primary importance in capillary gas chromatography. The performance of the sample introduction system is crucial for the overall chromatographic performance of the complete system. Much progress has been made in recent years, and our understanding of injection phenomena has increased tremendously. Because of the great variety of column characteristics (e.g., inner diameter, film thickness, sample capacity, carrier gas selection, and linear gas velocity, etc.) and the diversity of samples (e.g., wide range of component concentrations from highly volatile to less volatile components, different thermal stabilities, etc.), that can be analyzed with modern capillary GC, several injection modes have been developed. A final "universal" optimal approach to sample introduction, however, has not yet been determined; and it is questionable whether such an approach can be provided at all: "...there does not now and probably never will exist injector hardware or methodology that is suitable for all samples, under all conditions (2)." "There is still no such thing as a universal injection system and there probably never will be (3)."

This does not mean, however, that precise and accurate results cannot be generated with the different injection systems that have been developed over the past years. It is a prerequisite, though, to know the possibilities and the limitations of the available systems. In combination with a sufficient knowledge of the composition of the sample to be analyzed, a proper injector choice will guarantee good results. A qualitative and quantitative analysis means that the

chromatographically determined composition of the sample
corresponds to its actual composition. Possible difficulties
encountered in obtaining such data must be attributed to the
sampling technique, various column effects, detector effects,
or to a combination of all of these. A sample introduction
system can be "discriminative," meaning that certain
components are not quantitatively introduced into the column.
The column itself can also act discriminatingly (reversible
and/or irreversible adsorption), and can be injection-
dependent. The characteristics of the column in use,
therefore, have to be well established before any conclusion
can be drawn with regard to the sampling system.

The basic prerequisite of a sampling system for capillary gas
chromatography is that the sample be introduced into the
column as a narrow band, the composition of which is identical
to the original composition of the sample. The width of the inlet
band must be such that its variance is not significant as
compared with that due to the chromatographic peak
broadening process. The total measured variance (σ_m) is the
sum of all contributions to the peak variance:

$$\sigma_m^2 = \sigma_c^2 + \sigma_i^2 + \sigma_{ex}^2 \qquad \textbf{[Eq. 1]}$$

where

σ_m = measured peak variance (total band broadening)

σ_c = column peak variance

σ_i = inlet peak variance

σ_{ex} = extra-peak variance

With modern CGC instrumentation, the extra-peak variance contribution (electrometer, datasystem, recording)
approaches zero giving:

$$\sigma_m^2 = \sigma_c^2 + \sigma_i^2 \qquad \textbf{[Eq. 2]}$$

Due to the occurrence of the squared variances in this
equation, the contribution of the initial (inlet) band width to the
total peak band width is less dramatic than might be expected.
For example, a peak with chromatographic band broadening of
5 seconds shows a band broadening of 5.1 seconds when the
band width is 1 second—or 5.3 seconds if the injected band
width is 2 seconds. Therefore, on classical capillary columns,
injection band widths of 1 second are acceptable; with higher
capacity ratio (i.e., the higher the chromatographic band
broadening), initial band width becomes even less significant.

Two approaches are used to produce narrow initial (inlet)
bands:

1. Only very small samples (1 to 5 nl) are introduced into the
   column. A sample stream-splitting device (splitter)
   accomplishes this task. The sample vapor, formed upon
   injection at elevated temperature, is split into two sample
   streams of different flow rates. Cold splitting of the liquid
   sample is another possibility that has not yet been studied in
   depth.

2. The entire sample is introduced into the column. The broad
   initial band is immediately focused into a narrow initial band
   by sharpening mechanisms such as thermal, solvent,
   and/or stationary phase focusing. In practice, these effects
   are used to great advantage to focus the solute band widths
   produced by splitless, direct, and on-column injection.

In the subsequent sections, the most important sample introduction systems will be discussed in some detail:

1. Split injection
2. Splitless injection
3. On-column injection
4. Direct injection
5. Programmed temperature vaporizing injection

Emphasis will be placed on the performance of these systems in terms of quantitation. Selection criteria for typical applications, as well as their effect on the optimum column dimensions, will be discussed.

In the context of this book, it is impossible to treat every aspect of sample introduction in depth. Full details on the different sampling methods can be found in the excellent books of K. Grob Jr. (4,5). A survey of sampling systems is given in Sample Introduction in Capillary GC, Vol 1 (3) and Vol 2 (6).

Split Injection

Split sampling was the first sample introduction system developed for capillary gas chromatography (7). The conventional split injector is a flash vaporization device. The liquid plug, introduced with a syringe, is immediately volatilized and a small fraction of the resultant vapor enters the column while the major portion is vented to waste. This technique guarantees narrow inlet bands.

A schematic diagram of a split injector is shown in Figure 3-1. Preheated carrier gas, controlled by a pressure regulator or a combination of a flow controller and a back-pressure regulator (8), enters the injector. The flow is divided into two streams. One stream of carrier gas flows upward and purges the septum. The septum purge flow is controlled by a needle valve. Septum purge flow rates are usually between 3 and 5 ml/min. A high flow of carrier gas enters the vaporization chamber, which is a glass or quartz liner, where the vaporized sample is mixed with the carrier gas. The mixed stream is split at the column inlet, and only a small fraction enters the column. A needle valve or flow controller regulates the split ratio.

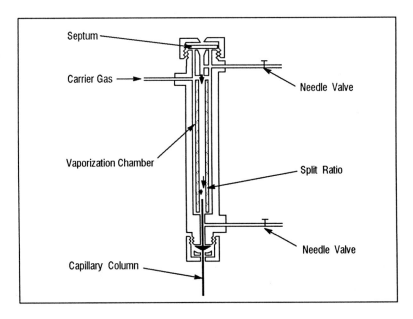

Figure 3-1.   Schematic diagram of a split injector.

Split ratios (column flow/inlet flow) typically range from 1:50 to 1:500 for conventional capillary columns (0.22 to 0.32 mm id). Lower split ratios may be used in combination with focusing effects. For high sample capacity columns, such as wide bore columns and/or thick film columns, low split ratios (1:5 to 1:50) are commonly used. In high-speed capillary gas chromatography, applying 50 to 100 μm id columns, split ratios can exceed 1:1000.

In split injection, initial band widths are very narrow. One must, however, take into consideration that sample size and split ratio must be adapted to the problem at hand.

For example:

Sample concentration:	0.01 to 0.1%
Per microliter:	0.1 to 1 μg
FID sensitivity:	$\approx$ 1 ng
Column:	25 m x 0.25 mm id,
d_f:	0.25 μm
Sample capacity column:	50 ng per compound
Volume insert:	1 ml (8 cm x 0.4 cm id)
Volume sample:	1 μl–0.4 ml vapor, diluted with carrier gas $\approx$ 0.8 ml

For a one-second initial band width, the flow through the inlet splitter must be 0.8 ml/sec or 50 ml/min. For a carrier gas flow of 2 ml/min this corresponds to a minimal split ratio of 1:25; for a flow of 1 ml/min to a split ratio of 1:50. This, of course, is only valid if focusing effects do not occur.

Because split injection is a flash vaporization technique, sample discrimination is difficult to avoid. This is especially the case if the sample is known to contain components in different concentrations and with different volatilities and polarities.

Sample discrimination in split injection is caused by inlet-related parameters as well as by operational parameters such as syringe handling.

Inlet-related discrimination is often referred to as nonlinearity of the splitter device. Linearity in this respect means that the split ratio at the point of splitting is equal to the preset split ratio and equal for all of the components in the sample. Linear splitting of varying sample components (concentration, volatility, or polarity) is impossible to achieve even when a sample is introduced in a nondiscriminating manner into the vaporization chamber.

Different mechanisms can cause nonlinear splitting:

1. Different diffusion speed of the sample components.

2. Incomplete evaporation.

3. Fluctuating split ratio.

The different mechanisms and their respective contributions are discussed thoroughly in Reference 4.

Nonlinearity can be minimized by complete vaporization of the sample, followed by homogeneous mixing with the carrier gas before the sample enters the column. Obvious as this may seem, a sample introduced by split injection often arrives at the point of splitting as a mixture of vapor and nonuniform droplets.

Two approaches can be used to minimize this phenomenon:
  – increase injection temperature,
  – optimize the inlet configuration and glass liners.

Different glass liners have been proposed (i.e., empty tube, short glass wool plug in the splitting region, short glass wool plug in the injection region, long and tight glass wool plug, packing with chromatographic support or glass beads, deformation of cross section, Jennings tube, etc.) to achieve efficient heat transfer to the injected sample and to ensure the thorough mixture of carrier gas with the vaporized sample. Although such modifications demonstrate an improvement in sample discrimination for some applications, the same setup may result in stronger discrimination for others.

A typical example of the positive effect of packing the glass liner can be found in the analysis of fatty acid methyl esters, obtained by methanolysis of oils or fats. Figure 3-2 shows the analysis of a fatty acid methyl ester (FAME) standard mixture and the configuration of the inlet. The percent composition of the FAMEs, ranging from C_{10} to C_{22}, can be determined with high precision and accuracy, applying the "fast hot needle injection" method of isooctane solutions in a wide bore glass liner, loosely packed with deactivated 100 μm glass beads. With a split ratio of 1:100, the residence time of the sample in the liner is very short. Additional heating will completely vaporize the sample and minimize discrimination.

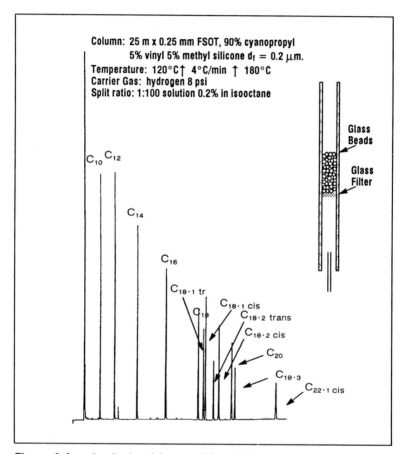

Figure 3-2.   Analysis of fatty acid methyl ester mixture.

For some other applications, however, the use of packed liners often results in peak broadening, especially if the support material is densely packed in the liner. This broadening is due to the multipath diffusion through the packing, the physical process in the inlet liner assuming no adsorption or partitioning occurs. Thermal focusing in the capillary column is often applied to avoid this. In most cases, the heat transfer capacity of an open liner will be sufficient to vaporize the sample. As a general rule, packed liners should not be used unless bad results have been obtained with an open liner. In essential oil analysis, for example, an open split liner guarantees the best results. Essential oils are complex mixtures that span a wide range of concentrations and polarities. The range of boiling points, however, is small enough for complete evaporation to take place in a properly heated open inlet (250°C–260°C). When using packed inserts for such applications, adsorption of polar solutes and degradation of labile solutes frequently occurs.

An extra advantage of split injection for essential oil analysis, or in the analysis of complex mixtures covering a relatively small range of boiling points in general, is that two columns can easily be connected to the same injection port. In this way, data are simultaneously generated on two different stationary phases with one single sample injection (9,10,11). A dual channel analysis of the sesquiterpene fraction of Patchouli Balsam is shown in Figure 3-3.

In comparison to injection techniques applying focusing effects, a benefit of split injection is the very reproducible retention data it provides. Retention indices on both columns may readily be calculated and compared to tabulated values (12).

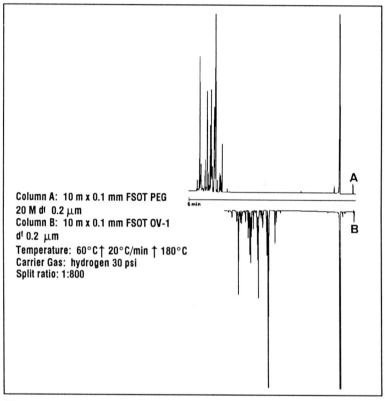

Column A: 10 m x 0.1 mm FSOT PEG
20 M d⁰ 0.2 μm
Column B: 10 m x 0.1 mm FSOT OV-1
d⁰ 0.2 μm
Temperature: 60°C† 20°C/min † 180°C
Carrier Gas: hydrogen 30 psi
Split ratio: 1:800

Figure 3-3.   Split dual channel analysis of the sesquiterpene
fraction of patchouli balsam.

In the previous discussion it was assumed that sample
introduction into the vaporization chamber with a syringe
occurs without any alteration to the sample.   In other words,
that no discrimination is caused by the syringe introduction.
However, most of the discrimination problems encountered
with vaporizing injectors are related to syringe needle effects.
Upon introducing the syringe needle through the septum,
volatiles immediately start to evaporate inside the needle itself,
which is heated by the injector. Also, after pushing down the
plunger, solvent and volatile solutes are evaporated more
readily than high-boiling solute material, which partially remains

on the needle wall. Removal of the needle from the injector body removes the nonvolatile components from the vaporization chamber as well, resulting in a mass discrimination according to volatility. A typical example of discrimination of n-alkanes in split injection is shown in Figure 3-4 (13).

Multiple methods of syringe manipulation have been studied (e.g., filled needle, cold needle, hot needle, solvent flush, air flush, sandwich method) in combination with fast or slow injection (13,14). This chapter will focus on "hot needle fast sample introduction." This method guarantees minimal syringe discrimination, although complete avoidance is not possible when dealing with solutes of a large volatility difference.

In the hot needle method, the sample is taken into the syringe barrel (for example, a 2 µl sample plug brought up to the 5 µl mark when using a 10 µl syringe) without leaving an air plug between sample and plunger. After insertion into the injection zone, the needle is allowed to heat up for 3 to 5 seconds. This period of time is sufficient for the needle to be heated to the injector temperature. The sample is then injected by rapidly pushing the plunger down (fast injection), after which the needle is withdrawn from the injector within one second. This technique has been evaluated by several researchers and appears to yield reproducible results.

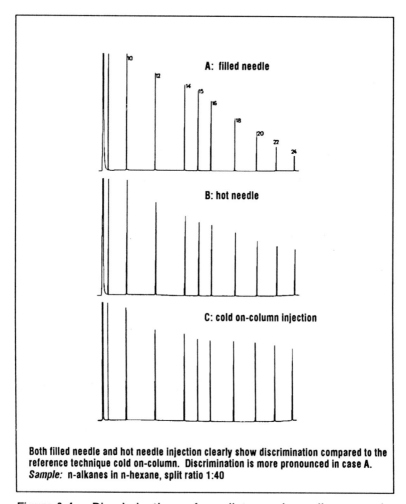

Both filled needle and hot needle injection clearly show discrimination compared to the reference technique cold on-column. Discrimination is more pronounced in case A. *Sample:* n-alkanes in n-hexane, split ratio 1:40

Figure 3-4. Discrimination of n-alkanes depending on the injection technique. (Reproduced with permission from Reference 13. Copyright Dr. A. Huethig Publishers.)

However, it is very important, to note that the physical condition of the syringe is crucial. Aging syringes exhibit characteristics such as leaky plunger-barrels, distorted plungers, etc., which must be avoided at any price. In the same context, only a clean vaporizing tube guarantees good qualitative and quantitative data. The influence of a dirty vaporizing inlet on chromatographic performance is illustrated in Figure 3-5 (15).

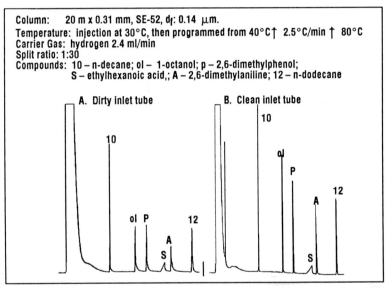

Figure 3-5.   Influence of a dirty vaporizing injector (200°C). (Reproduced with permission from Reference 15. Copyright Dr. A. Huethig Publishers.)

Syringe discrimination is strongly related to the warming of the needle in the vaporization chamber. It is possible to develop systems in which syringe discrimination is reduced or avoided.

Delayed warming of the needle can be achieved by:
- Cooled-needle injection.
- Very fast injection.
- Programmed temperature vaporizing (PTV) injection.

With the cooled-needle technique (16), the needle is cooled during the injection so that selective evaporation cannot occur. The very fast injection method (17) does not give the needle time to warm up. Both techniques are described briefly. Programmed temperature vaporizing injection is treated separately.

Figure 3-6 schematically depicts the principle of cooled-needle split injection. The syringe needle is cooled during its stay in the inlet by circulating cold air or gaseous CO_2 in the cooling device. Only the tip of the needle (2 to 3 mm) enters into the hot vaporization chamber. Cooling down of the wide bore glass liner is avoided by proper insulation of the cooling device. The cooled-needle technique was developed to avoid selective vaporization from the syringe needle and to minimize the impact of syringe manipulation (16,18). This last point is very important because manual split injection can provide precise and accurate results based on relative peak areas but seldom on absolute peak areas. The internal standard method, therefore, is the method of choice in split injection. With the cooled-needle technique, the precision and accuracy of absolute and relative peak areas of a hydrocarbon test mixture, ranging from C_{10} to C_{32}, are excellent. Automation of the cooled-needle split injection (automatic sampling) is feasible.

Automatic sampling can be considered a prerequisite for obtaining optimal reproducibility; every step of the injection sequence is identical for each injection. This condition is even more stringent for the very fast injection technique, which cannot be achieved manually. The objective of very fast injection is to get the needle into the injection port, inject the sample, and withdraw the needle so quickly that it has no time to warm up. This eliminates sample evaporation. In addition, fast injection implies that the delivered volume of sample equals the preset sample volume. The effect of the needle dwell time in the injection port on sample discrimination has been studied (17). Dwell time is defined as the interval

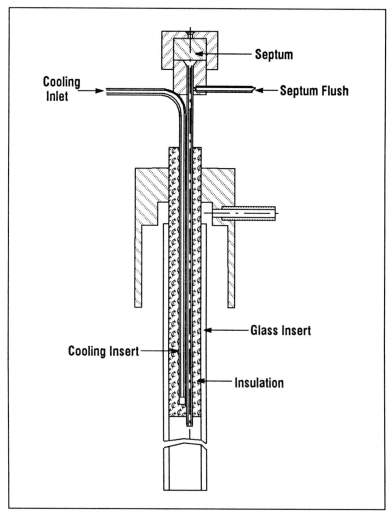

Figure 3-6. Cooled-needle split injection. (Reproduced with permission from Reference 18. Copyright Dr. A. Huethig Publishers.)

between the needle tip piercing the bottom of the septum on the way in and reaching the same point on the way out. Figure 3-7 shows a plot of C_X/C_{20} area ratios (x = 10 to 40) as a function of the carbon number for different dwell times, using hexane as the solvent. Although these data have been obtained for direct injection, they are also valid for split injection. A dwell time of 500 ms or less shows no noticeable fractionation.

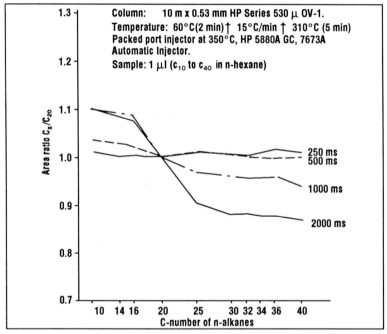

Figure 3-7.   Effect of needle dwell time on the injection port fractionation.

Figure 3-8 shows the results obtained using an automatic sampler for a 100 ms injection for a packed column and capillary split injection, in comparison to manual direct injection and on-column injection. All data are normalized to cold on-column injection results for the same sample. Cold on-column injection features neither needle nor inlet fractionation. The slight deviation from linearity for the split injection is caused by inlet nonlinearity rather than by needle discrimination. Considering that this technique is a cold-filled needle injection system, the results are surprisingly good.

From the previous discussion, it is obvious that obtaining quantitative data using a split injector can be problematic but not impossible. To reduce fractionation or discrimination as a function of sample volatility, the injection technique must be optimized. This is most easily accomplished and the greatest precision and accuracy achieved when samples having similar volatility are used.

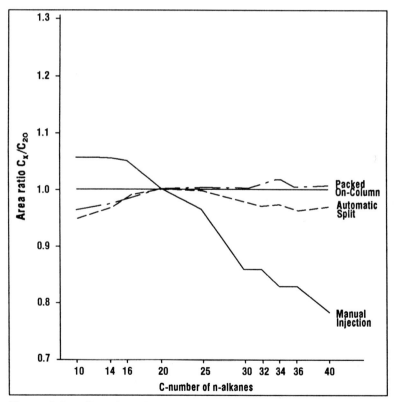

Figure 3-8.   Fractionation performance.

Guidelines for Split Injection

- For quantitation, the standard addition or the internal standard method is preferred. The external standard method in which absolute peak areas are compared can be used with either the cooled-needle injection technique, programmed temperature vaporization, or fast automated injection.

- Reproducibility will be enhanced by not varying the injected volume, which typically should be 0.5 µl to 2.0 µl.

- Injector temperature should be adapted to the problem at hand. Excessively high injector temperatures should be avoided.

- The hot-needle fast injection method is preferred for manual injection.

- The use of highly volatile solvents should be avoided whenever possible.

- If an open liner does not do the job, loose packing with deactivated glass wool or glass beads can provide a solution. One should be aware, however, of adsorption and decomposition risks.

- One of the main problems associated with split injection is syringe handling. The use of an automatic sampling system can overcome this difficulty.

For several applications, however, split injection will not give high quantitative accuracy. Unfortunately, some samples by nature require the use of split injection, e.g., samples that cannot be diluted (thinners, solvents, headspace, gaseous samples, etc.). Figure 3-9 shows an analysis of the impurities in styrene. For this particular application, the reproducibility and accuracy obtained with split injection is superior to that of other injection techniques.

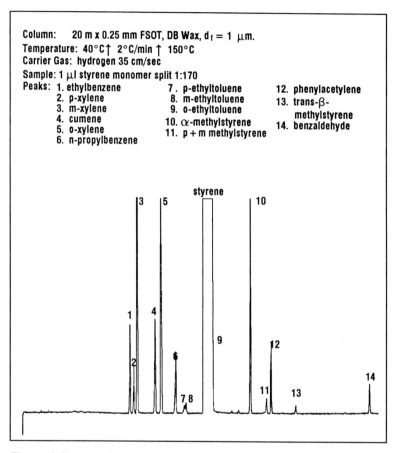

Figure 3-9.   Analysis of styrene monomer.   (Courtesy of R. Miller, Huntsman Chemical Corporation.)

In another example of these sample types, the analysis of Dutch natural gas is shown in Figure 3-10. One milliliter of gas was introduced to quantify the minor components. The excellent peak shape of the compounds eluting after propane is due to the stationary phase focusing on the aluminum oxide adsorbent.

Other fields where, up to now, split injection is the only applicable technique include high speed chromatography and ultrahigh resolution capillary gas chromatography using 50 to 100 μm id capillary columns (19,20). Very small initial band widths are necessary to fully exploit the high efficiency of ultranarrow bore columns.

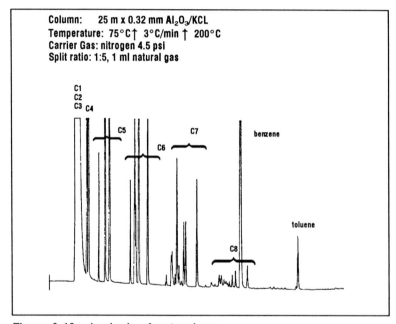

Figure 3-10. Analysis of natural gas.

Figure 3-11 shows the analysis of diesel oil using a 100 m x 100 μm capillary column, generating 1,000,000 theoretical plates. One-tenth microliter of diesel oil was injected with a split ratio of 1:300.

Splitless Injection

Splitless injection in capillary gas chromatography was developed as the result of a bad injection. By accident, Grob Sr. injected a sample into a split injector while the split valve was closed. To his big surprise, the eluting peaks were not abnormally broad. Grob's fundamental study of the phenomena explaining these experimental observations resulted in the development of splitless injection (21,22).

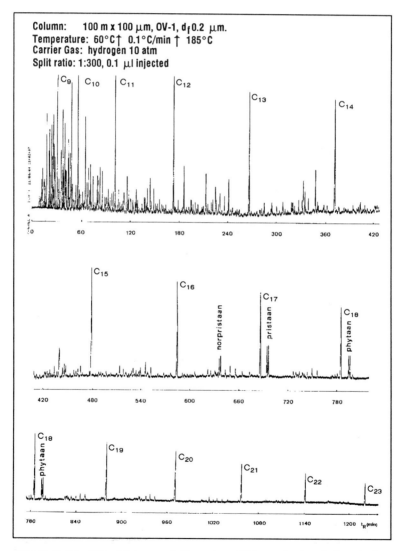

Figure 3-11. Ultrahigh resolution (n = 10⁶) analysis of diesel oil.

In splitless injection, a conventional split injector is operated in a nonsplitting mode by closing the split valve during injection. The sample is flash vaporized in the vaporizing chamber, and from there the sample vapors are carried onto the column by the mobile phase flow. Since this transfer takes several hundred milliseconds, broad initial band widths would be anticipated. However, through optimal use of focusing effects, such as solvent, thermal, and stationary phase focusing, initial peak broadening can be suppressed.

The main benefit of splitless injection lies in the fact that the total injected sample is introduced into the column; this results in a much higher sensitivity than that achieved using split injection. For a long time splitless injection was the only sample introduction technique used in capillary GC for trace analysis.

A schematic representation of a purged splitless injector and the pneumatic configurations involved in an injection sequence are shown in Figure 3-12. The pneumatic configuration is similar to that of the classical split injector. The septum is continuously purged (2 ml/min) to maintain a contamination free system, while a flow of 20 to 50 ml/min passes the split outlet (Figure 3-12A). Prior to injection, a solenoid valve is activated so that the split line is closed off while the septum purge is maintained. Figure 3-12B shows the splitless inlet configuration at injection. After waiting a sufficient time for the solvent-solute vapor to be transferred onto the column (i.e., 30–80 seconds), the solenoid valve is deactivated. Residual vapors in the vaporizing chamber are vented to waste via the split line. For this reason, in splitless injection the split line is often referred to as the purge line.

The carrier gas flow rate through the inlet as a function of time for the splitless sampling mode is shown in Figure 3-13. The time interval between the point of injection and the activation of the split-purge line is a function of the characteristics of solvent and solutes, the volume of the vaporizing chamber, the sample size, the injection speed, and the carrier gas velocity.

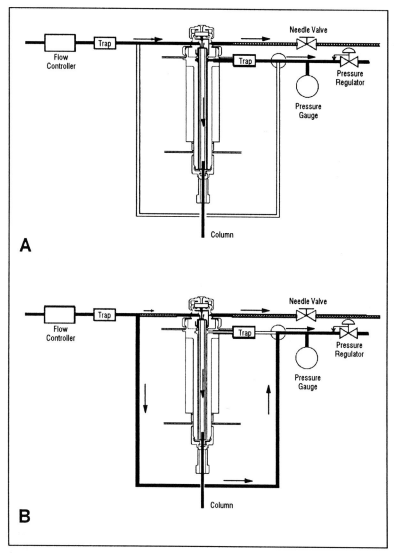

Figure 3-12. A. A schematic representation of a spitless inlet
before and after injection.
B. The splitless inlet configuration at injection.
Carrier gas flow paths are indicated.

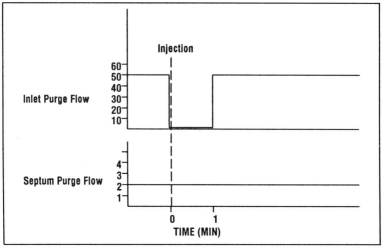

Figure 3-13. Carrier gas flow rate (ml/min) through the inlet as a function of time for the splitless (60 sec) sampling mode.

The interdependence of the factors affecting the time interval between the point of injection and the activation of the split purge line is shown by the following example:

Assume a sample concentration of 20 ppm n-C12 to n-C16 in isooctane

Per microliter:	20 ng
FID-sensitivity:	$\approx$ 1 ng
Insert volume:	0.6 ml (8 cm x 0.31 mm id)
Sample volume:	0.4 ml of sample vapor, diluted with carrier gas $\approx$ 0.6 ml

For a carrier gas hydrogen flow rate of 2 ml/min, the splitless time must be at least 30 seconds. Because of the exponential dilution, it is recommended that the splitless time be 1.5 times the time required for the carrier gas to sweep the injector volume, i.e., 45 seconds.

The sample transfer from the vaporizing chamber into the column is a slow process. Solvent vapors especially tend to remain in the inlet for a long time. Purging the insert after the injection will remove the last traces of vapor from the vaporizing chamber. Figure 3-14 shows the effect of inlet purging on the solvent peak shape in comparison to the same injection without inlet purging. The amount of sample that is lost by activating the purge line during a splitless injection is small, provided all parameters are optimized. The septum purge flow rate also has an effect on the quantitative transfer of the solutes onto the column. Sample material is lost through the septum purge line if the insert is overfilled with sample vapors.

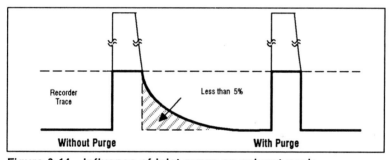

Figure 3-14. Influence of inlet purge on solvent peak.

Septum purge flow rate is illustrated in Figure 3-15. Low septum purge flow rates and sample sizes of 1 to 2 µl do not create problems in this respect. An important aspect in the design of a splitless injector is the dimension of the vaporizing chamber. Long and narrow inserts are preferred to obtain minimal sample dilution. Internal volumes vary between 0.5 ml and 1 ml. The column is installed 0.5 cm into the insert and syringes with long needles are used creating a distance of 1 cm to 1.5 cm between the needle tip and the column inlet. Overfilling of the vaporizing chamber is suppressed, and fast sample transfer is achieved. Due to the relatively long residence time of the solutes in the vaporizing chamber, lower injection temperatures can be used as compared with split injection. This helps to minimize sample degradation as does the use of nonpacked inserts.

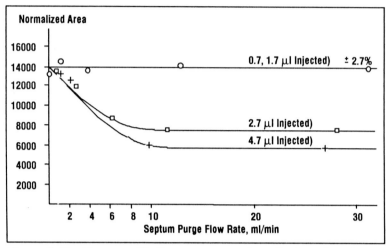

Figure 3-15. The quantitative recovery of n-C$_{11}$ is a function of the septum purge flow rate of a range of injected volumes.

Figure 3-16 shows the effect of the injection port temperature on the chromatographic profile; the analysis of styrene is highlighted. The temperature of the injection port can function as a peak generator. Note that not only are there more peaks obtained at higher injection port temperatures, but the peak ratios of the "real" peaks (as determined using on-column injection) also vary as the port temperature increases. On-column injection provides the most accurate representation of the sample. Syringe discrimination, which is one of the largest sources of error when applying vaporizing injection, is also evident from Figure 3-16. In the on-column injection trace, the peak height ratio of the triphenyl hexene (x) over the diphenylcyclobutane (y) is 1.35; whereas in splitless injection at 200°C, the ratio is only 0.84. The syringe needle discrimination in this case exceeds 33%! In splitless injection, the samples very often contain heavy by-products (i.e., environmental samples, biological samples, etc.). At low inlet temperatures the nonvolatile matrix retains the solutes of interest. To enhance diffusion out of such matrices, high temperatures are required.

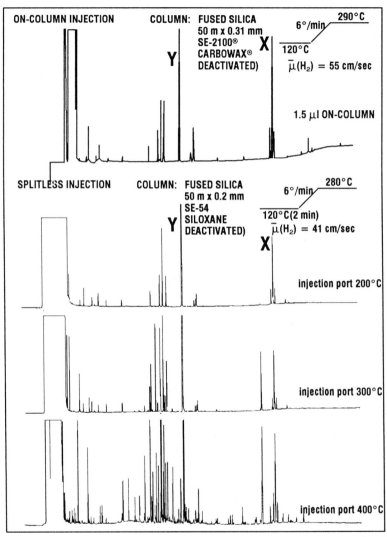

Figure 3-16. These four chromatograms of styrene obtained using on-column and splitless sampling show the effect the injection port temperature can have on the peak profile. The splitless chromatograms were kindly supplied by Mr. Roger Miller, Huntsman Chemical Corporation.

The performance of a splitless injector for a particular application depends on the optimization of experimental variables. The most important variables include sample size, injection speed, purge time, injection temperature, initial column temperature, carrier gas selection, and flow rate. General guidelines cannot be advanced, and some of the variables can only be determined by trial and error.

Whatever the application, however, refocusing of the solutes in the inlet section of the capillary column is necessary. In splitless injection, the initial band widths are broadened by two mechanisms—band broadening in time and band broadening in space (4,23,24).

Band broadening in time is caused by the slow transfer from the vaporizing chamber to the column inlet section, which takes several hundred milliseconds. Once in the column, the solutes spread over a portion of the column length, mainly by flooding of the sample liquid, thus causing band broadening in space. The fundamental difference between band broadening in time and band broadening in space is that, in the first case, solutes are spread equally with respect to gas chromato-graphic retention time; whereas, in the second case, solutes are spread equally with respect to the column length. Both phenomena cause distorted elution profiles if the solutes are not refocused before starting the chromatographic distribution process.

Band broadening in time is suppressed by solvent focusing or by thermal focusing, also referred to as cold trapping.

The "Solvent Effect"

To make use of the solvent effect for reconcentrating solutes in the column, the column temperature during injection must be 25 to 30°C below the boiling point of the solvent. The vaporized solvent is condensed in the column inlet where it is retained by the stationary phase. The liquid plug formed in this way temporarily behaves as a thick stationary phase film, retaining the vaporized solutes. In other words, the solvent acts as a kind of barrier to the sample components. The thick solvent film creates a section in the capillary column inlet with a lowered β-value. As described in Chapter 1, the β-value is defined as the ratio of the volume of mobile phase (V_m) over the volume of stationary phase (V_s),

$$\beta = V_m/V_s \qquad \text{[Eq. 3]}$$

Decrease of β will cause a corresponding increase of the partition ratio, k

$$k = K_D/\beta \qquad \text{[Eq. 4]}$$

in which K_D is the partition coefficient. The resulting large k-values account for the reconcentration of sample solutes in the column inlet section. After the transfer from the vaporizing chamber into the column, the purge line is activated and the column oven temperature is increased; the solvent evaporates, and the solutes start the chromatographic process with small initial band widths.

Thermal Focusing

Thermal focusing or "cold trapping" is performed at column temperatures low enough to condense the components of interest but sufficiently high to evaporate the solvent. Under these conditions it is not possible to achieve a solvent effect. In practice however, solute reconcentration very often is a combination of solvent focusing and thermal focusing. Thermal focusing or cold trapping will narrow the band widths effectively if there is a sufficient temperature difference ($\geq 150°C$) between the column temperature and the boiling points of the solutes. An example of condensing at the head of the column is shown in Figure 3-17.

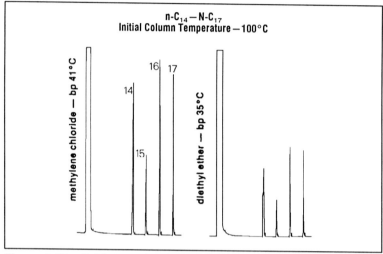

Figure 3-17. Cold trapping in the splitless injection mode.

At 100°C there is no solvent effect with either dichloromethane or diethyl ether. The hydrocarbons C_{15}, C_{16}, C_{17} (boiling points 270, 286, and 302°C, respectively) are effectively cold trapped on the first few centimeters of the column, and have good peak shape. Broadening of C_{14} (boiling point 254°C) is not completely avoided, but the peak shape is not really distorted. The thickness of the stationary phase also has an effect on the retention power in thermal focusing. The headspace analysis of a copolymer of styrene, methyl-methacrylate, and butylacrylate is shown in Figure 3-18. One-milliliter headspace was splitless injected (purge time 60 sec) on a 50 m x 0.25 mm id column coated with a 1 μm film of OV-101. The oven temperature was 20°C during injection and, after one minute, programmed ballistically to 60°C and then to 120°C at 6°C/min. Figure 3-18A shows the analysis of the copolymer spiked with 1 ppm MMA and styrene and 300 ppb BA. The compounds of interest are nicely focused, whereas, the early eluting peaks are strongly distorted due to band broadening in time. Figure 3-18B shows the analysis of an unspiked sample.

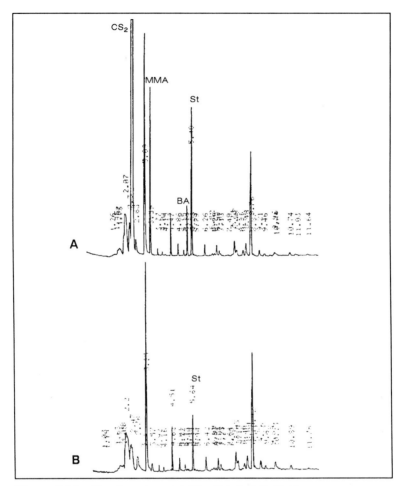

Figure 3-18. Headspace analysis of a copolymer.

Cold trapping occurs automatically in programmed temperature runs. This is illustrated in Figure 3-19, which shows the analysis of diesel fuel dissolved in n-pentane in the split (A) and splitless (B) modes. In the split mode, all hydrocarbons from C_9 to C_{22} elute with perfect peak shape. In the splitless mode, at 50°C and using pentane as the solvent, the early eluted peaks are broadened as there is no solvent effect.

Due to increasing reconcentration by cold trapping, broadening diminishes with increasing carbon numbers. The C_{14} peak is perfectly shaped. Under the same experimental conditions and using isooctane instead of n-pentane, the peak profiles in splitless injection would be similar to those using split injection. The first eluting compounds would benefit from the solvent effect and the later eluting compounds from cold trapping.

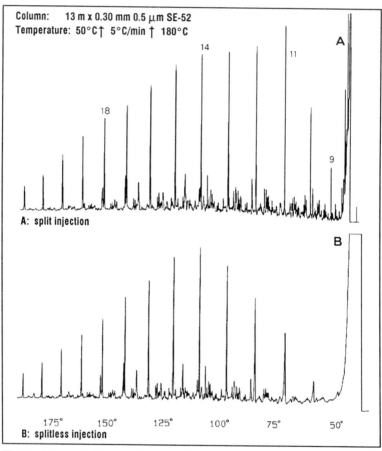

Figure 3-19. Cold-trapping effect during a temperature programmed run. (Reproduced with permission from Reference 4. Copyright Dr. A. Huethig Publishers.)

Band broadening in space was only discovered in 1981 (23) and is a direct consequence of the solvent effect. As a result of the solvent effect, solute bands that were broadened in time are refocused on a thick layer of solvent. Upon condensation, however, the solvent layer in the first few centimeters of the column becomes too thick to be stable. The carrier gas pushes the plug further into the column, creating a "flooded zone" (Figure 3-20). The solute material is then spread over the full length of the flooded zone, thus creating a solute band width which equals the length of the flooded zone. For 1 µl injections, the length of the flooded zone is roughly 20–30 cm provided the stationary phase is perfectly wetted by the solvent (i.e., isooctane solutions on apolar dimethylsilicone phases, ethylacetate solutions on polyethylene glycol phases).

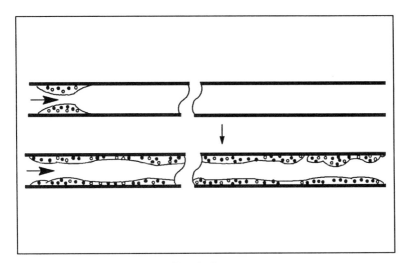

Figure 3-20. Creation of a flooded zone.

On conventional capillary columns, 25–30 m in length with an id of 0.32 mm and a sample volume of 1 µl, band broadening will hardly be observed as no peak distortion occurs. Only careful evaluation of the chromatogram will show whether or not band broadening has occurred. A typical example of band broadening in space was published by K. Grob Jr. (24).

In the Grob study, fatty acid methyl esters C_6 to C_{18} dissolved in different solvents, were analyzed with splitless injection. For comparison, split injection was done as well. Figure 3-21A shows the split injection chromatogram in which band broadening does not occur. The splitless injection at 25°C of an n-hexane solution is depicted in Figure 3-21B. The solvent is recondensed in the inlet section of the column, and the solutes are spread over the flooded zone. All peaks are broadened by about 30%, except for C_6 which is fully reconcentrated at the spot where the last part of the solvent evaporates (solvent effect). When injecting the same sample at 60°C, the solvent effect is minimal, and peak broadening in space does not occur (Figure 3-21C). The fact that C_6 and C_8 are broadened is now due to band broadening in time and the absence of the solvent effect. As already mentioned, band broadening in space is not observed often because the peaks are not really distorted. If, on the other hand, the solvent does not wet the stationary phase sufficiently well, as is the case for polar solvents such as methane on apolar phases, distorted peaks will be created. This is because the flooded zone is longer (several meters) and, moreover, will be composed of inhomogeneous droplets. This is illustrated in Figure 3-21D showing the analysis of fatty acid methyl esters with methanol as the solvent. Note the peak distortion and splitting.

Retention Gap

Band broadening in space can be suppressed by stationary phase focusing via a retention gap (25,26). A retention gap is a specified length of uncoated column. All solutes, therefore, will have a k-value which is close to zero. Upon evaporation of the solvent, all the solutes which are spread over the flooded zone are carried onto the stationary phase where they are retained. Figure 3-22 illustrates this. In practice, the retention gap can be that portion of the column from which the stationary phase has been rinsed or a separate piece of deactivated fused silica connected to the analytical column through a coupling device.

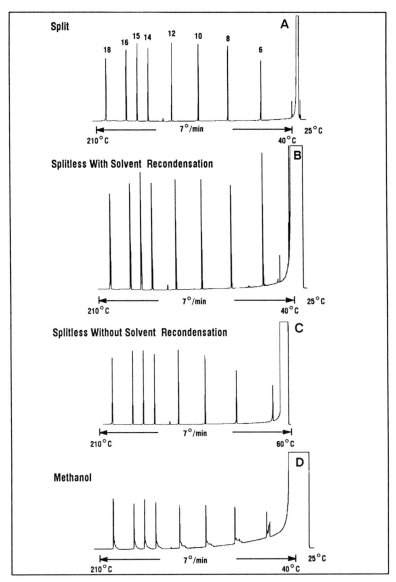

Figure 3-21. Band broadening in space in splitless injection.
(Reproduced with permission from Reference 24.
Copyright Dr. A. Huethig Publishers.)

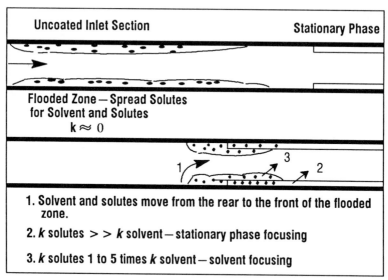

Figure 3-22. Working mechanism of a retention gap.

To use an uncoated portion of the column as the retention gap, chromatographers must prepare their own columns since most commercial columns contain stationary phases that have been immobilized. The length of the retention gap is a function of the length of the flooded zone and, therefore, will depend on the sample volume and the nature of the solvent used. Typical lengths are 0.5 m to 1.0 m for injections of 1 μl to 2 μl.

The retention gap must be deactivated properly using a procedure that is suitable for the application for which the gap will be used. The solvent must wet the surface homogeneously to obtain good reconcentration. For apolar solvents, deactivation is best performed with apolar silylating agents such as HMDS or D4. For increased polarity, phenyl-containing silylating agents have to be applied (i.e., diphenyl-tetramethylsilazane or tetraphenyldimethylsilylsilazane). The higher the polarity of the solvent used, the higher the phenyl content of the deactivating agent must be. For extreme cases, such as the injection of water or methanol, deactivation by coating the retention gap with a very thin film of immobilized polyethylene glycol (d_f = 0.01 μm) yields acceptable results. Band broadening in space and the use of a retention gap is further discussed in the section on cold on-column injection.

In recent years, splitless injection has been overshadowed by cold on-column injection. Nowadays, without any doubt, the most accurate and precise data are provided using on-column injection. However, splitless injection is still used for many routine determinations (i.e., in environmental analysis, pesticide monitoring, drug screening, etc.). In these fields sample preparation is of main concern, and it is not always possible or economically justified to clean up a sample to such an extent that the sample is compatible with on-column injection. Traces of involatiles or high boiling components often remain in samples. Splitless injection is an easy solution to such problems. The "dirty" sample components remain mostly in the vaporizing inlet, which is easily accessible for cleaning.

Figure 3-23 is an illustration of the determination of PCBs in waste oil. A simple sample preparation procedure was developed, based on liquid-liquid partition (acetonitrile/n-hexane) and solid phase cleanup on aminopropyl silica (27). The sample thus obtained is strongly enriched in PCBs but traces of mineral oils are still present. In splitless injection at 280°C, these components are not vaporized and remain in the inlet, which can easily be cleaned at the end of a working day. The waste oil in the case of Figure 3-23 contained 7.0 ppm Arochlor-1260.

Another reason why the disadvantages of splitless injection are often accepted is that accuracy and reproducibility requirements in trace analysis are not always that stringent. Indeed, the difference between 0.9 ppb and 1.1 ppb of lindane being present in a food sample is not relevant with regard to the practical conclusions to be drawn. Would it be worth the cost of three more clean-up steps to be able to state that the real concentration is 1.05 ppb ±0.03? What is the clinical

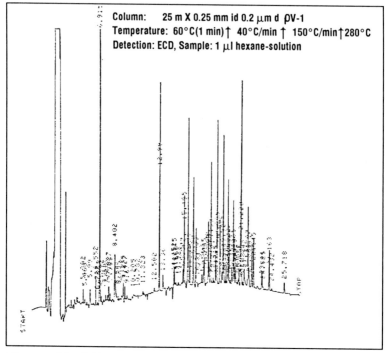

Figure 3-23. PCBs in waste oil. Splitless injection.

significance of a urinary steroid being present in a concentration of 2.0 ppm or 2.4 ppm? Reproducibility in splitless injection can be as good as ±1–2% SD (28). Standard addition or internal standard methods may be used to improve quantitation. The external standard method is easily adapted for automated splitless injection. However, the possibility of matrix effects must be taken into consideration. For capillary GC applications which require the best attainable precision and accuracy, splitless injection is not the method of choice.

Guidelines for Splitless Injection

● For splitless injection quantitation, both standard addition and the internal standard methods can be applied. Reproducibility of sample injection volume, (typically between 1 μl and 2 μl) is required.

● Reproducibility of sample volume is also a prerequisite for reproducible retention times.

● Reproducibility, both in retention time and quantitative data, is significantly improved by applying automatic injectors (28).

● For the analysis of volatiles with boiling points of less than 150°C, the initial band widths should be reduced by applying the solvent effect. For relatively high boiling components, cold trapping will focus the initial bands sufficiently. For unknown samples, both solvent effect and cold trapping can be achieved by operating in the temperature-programmed mode.

● To obtain an efficient solvent effect, the oven must be cooled to 20 to 30°C below the boiling point of the solvent.

● The hot-needle injection technique is preferred for manual injections. The sample feed rate should not exceed 1 μl– 2 μl per second.

● The injection temperature suited for a particular application is a function of the sample matrix. A temperature in the range of 200°C to 280°C will be sufficient for most applications. Very "dirty" samples require higher temperatures (300°C).

● Cleaning the injector regularly is beneficial.

● Fast carrier gasses, such as helium or hydrogen, must be used at flow rates exceeding 2 ml/min.

- A longer purge delay time (50 to 80 seconds) for most applications is better than short delay times (20 to 40 seconds).

- Splitless injection cannot be used to analyze solutes eluting ahead of the solvent. The peaks are broadened and distorted mostly by mechanisms such as partial solvent trapping and phase soaking (29).

- For polar solvents, the use of a retention gap strongly improves peak profiles.

On-Column Injection

On-column devices (micro and macro) were originally introduced in 1977 by Schomburg et al. (32). Because stringent technical requirements were necessary for the effective use of these devices, they lacked practical flexibility. In 1978 the Grobs (30,31) described syringe on-column injection on 0.32 mm id small capillary columns. The on-column injection process described by the Grobs requires that the id of the column and the od of the needle be correctly dimensioned and positioned. The design of the inlet as described by Grob is shown in Figure 3-24. A standard microliter syringe, fitted with a 0.23 mm (32 gauge) needle 7.5 cm in length, is inserted through the conical aperture until it is positioned just before the stop valve. The 0.3 mm inlet channel is almost completely blocked by the needle. Upon opening the valve, due to the created restriction, there is hardly any pressure drop at the column inlet. The syringe is pushed down and the needle is inserted into the 0.32 mm id column. The syringe plunger is depressed (the speed of the injection depends on the sample volume) and the liquid plug is introduced onto the column. After injection, the syringe is retracted to the same point above the stop valve, the position of which is indicated by an external mark. The valve is then closed and the needle is withdrawn. The whole injection system is permanently cooled by cold air or water circulation.

The cold on-column injection device was further refined by Galli, Trestianu, and Grob Jr. (33,34). The refinements include an auxiliary cooling system (secondary cooling) which was installed at the injector base located in the GC oven. A stream of air, introduced through a jacket surrounding the capillary column inlet, is directed towards the injection section of the column. This secondary cooling system completely eliminates syringe discrimination. Moreover, it allows the column oven to be operated at temperatures above the boiling point of the solvent. The capillary column inlet section is sufficiently cooled to eliminate evaporation. On-column injection onto 0.22 mm to 0.25 mm capillary columns became possible through the introduction of fused silica needles with outside diameters from 0.14 mm to 0.18 mm which also offer excellent inertness. The capillary channel shown in Figure 3-24 is reduced to 0.20 mm. An additional benefit of on-column systems is that septa, used for conventional split-splitless devices, are no longer required.

Since this pioneering work, a number of cold on-column injectors have been introduced.

Hinshaw and Yang developed a programmed-temperature on-column injector (35), in which the column inlet temperature is completely independent of the column oven temperature. The temperature of the column inlet, where the liquid sample is introduced, can be programmed linearly from subambient temperatures to 350°C at rates from 20°C to 180°C/min.

A simple on-column injection device was described by R. Freeman et al. (36) and K. Knauss et al. (37). A cross-section of the injector is presented in Figure 3-25. The injector has a low thermal mass, facilitating cooling. A key part of the injector is the duckbill valve. The duckbill valve, made of a soft elastomer, is a passive element in that there are no moving parts. It simply consists of two surfaces pressed together by the column inlet pressure. During injection, the syringe needle slips between the two surfaces maintaining the seal (Figure 3-26). The operation of the injector is outlined as follows: The required amount of sample is withdrawn from the sample vial using a syringe equipped with a fused silica needle (105 mm long, 0.14 mm od). Excess sample is wiped from the outside of the needle prior to injection. The needle guide is

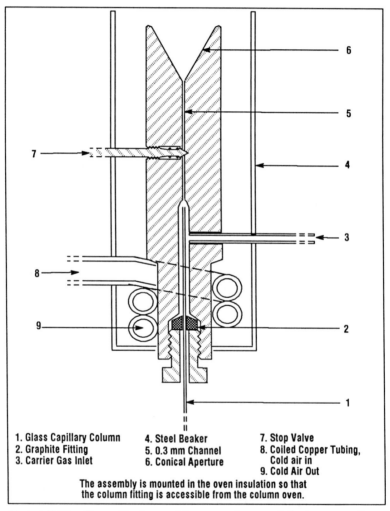

1. Glass Capillary Column   4. Steel Beaker   7. Stop Valve
2. Graphite Fitting   5. 0.3 mm Channel   8. Coiled Copper Tubing,
3. Carrier Gas Inlet   6. Conical Aperture   Cold air in
                                          9. Cold Air Out
The assembly is mounted in the oven insulation so that
the column fitting is accessible from the column oven.

Figure 3-24. The Grob cold on-column injector. From Reference 30, reprinted by permission of Elsevier, Amsterdam.

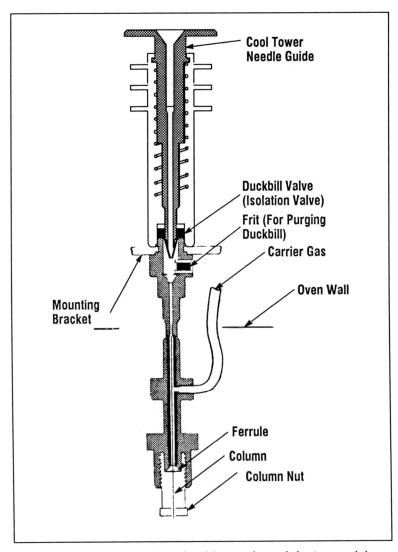

Cool Tower
Needle Guide

Duckbill Valve
(Isolation Valve)

Frit (For Purging
Duckbill)

Carrier Gas

Oven Wall

Mounting
Bracket

Ferrule

Column

Column Nut

Figure 3-25. Cross-section of cold on-column injector applying a
duckbill valve. For automated injections the duckbill
valve is replaced by a disk septum.

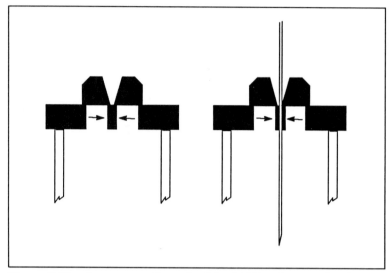

Figure 3-26. A cross-section of a "duckbill" valve used to isolate the chromatographic system. The arrows show how the inlet pressure serves to seal the valve.

depressed. This parts the surfaces of the isolation valve. The needle is then pushed through the needle guide and into the column. The needle guide opens the isolation valve, which prevents contact between the needle and the soft valve. No material from the valve can adhere to the column and inadvertently be introduced into the column. The isolation valve is continuously purged. Immediately below the valve is a frit that serves as a vent for the valve purge. Once the needle is well into the column, the needle guide is released; this withdraws the needle guide from the duckbill valve and tightens the valve against the syringe needle. The syringe plunger is then rapidly depressed and the syringe is immediately withdrawn.

Geeraert et al. developed a movable on-column injector for high temperature capillary gas chromatography (3,38,39). A movable on-column injector can move up and down the column oven wall. In the up position, the inlet section of the capillary column is situated outside the GC oven. Injection can thus be performed at ambient temperature. The solvent evaporates while the high boiling components are cold-trapped in the column inlet section. After complete elution of the solvent, which can be monitored by the FID detector, the injector is pushed down transporting the inlet section of the column through the oven wall into the GC oven, which is at analytical temperature, and the sample components partition through the column. The main advantage of the movable on-column injector lies in the fact that cold on-column injection can be performed at high oven temperatures. The principal of operation, in fact, is very similar to that of the solid-state injector (40). A movable on-column injector has also been developed by Jennings (41). Automated high oven temperature cold on-column injection was recently described (42). Excellent results were reported for lipid analysis. The secondary cooling tube, introduced by Galli et al.(33,34), is extended so that a column inlet temperature of 60°C can be attained for a 300°C oven temperature. A short precolumn is connected to the analytical column to allow automation.

A simple and versatile cold on-column injector was introduced by E. Dawes (43). The injector is equipped with a pneu-matically operated silicone rubber valve that seals around the syringe needle during injection. The injector is cooled by compressed air.

Most of the systems discussed have been developed for high resolution separations, (i.e., applying capillary columns ranging from 0.22 to 0.32 mm id). It is obvious that the same devices can be used for wide bore columns (0.53 mm id). For that type of column, however, the construction can be much simpler. Wide bore columns accept standard 0.47 mm od (26 gauge) needles, allowing the use of conventional GC septa. An example of a simple laboratory-made cold on-column injector can be found in Reference 44. For automated cold on-column injection, the system represented in Figure 3-25 has been modified with a disk septum so that a 26-gauge steel needle can be introduced into 530 μm capillary columns (45).

Most of the currently available cold on-column injection systems are pressure regulated. Pressure regulation not only provides for simpler design, but systems do not have to be completely leak-tight. During the injection procedure, a small leak is created; therefore, flow regulators cannot be used. In addition, flow-regulated systems do not allow purging of the on-column injector. Some systems apply pressure regulation during injection and switch over to flow regulation during analysis.

The advent of cold on-column injection has extended the range of applicability of capillary GC to include many classes of compounds which until now were difficult, if not impossible, to analyze. The technique of introducing the sample directly onto the column without prior vaporization offers a number of advantages, which can be summarized as follows:

- elimination of sample discrimination
- elimination of sample alteration
- high analytical precision
- data operator independence

Moreover, recent developments in GC hardware make cold on-column injection accessible to automation.

As with all other sampling techniques, operational parameters strongly affect the chromatographic data. Parameters such as initial column temperature, solvent nature, injection rate, injected volume, and boiling point range of the sample components are interrelated. Once again, in the context of this book, it is impossible to treat all aspects in detail. The book "On-column Injection in Capillary GC" by K. Grob contains 590 pages (5)! On-column injection is ideally suited for the introduction of large sample volumes. This possibility has lent itself to the logical combination of on-line HPLC (high-pressure liquid chromatography) and CGC (capillary gas chromatography) (46,47).

The discussion presented here mainly concerns sample sizes from 0.5 µl to 2 µl. The characteristics of the technique are highlighted, and important aspects for daily practical use are discussed.

For sample sizes in the range from 0.5 µl to 2 µl, injection should be performed as fast as possible with the column oven temperature below or equal to the boiling point of the solvent. Figure 3-27 shows that, with a slow injection, part of the sample may adhere to the needle. The longer the needle withdrawal time, the more volatiles are carried into the column by the carrier gas and the more heavy components stick to the needle wall. On the other hand, with fast injection the sample is sprayed into the column, away from the needle, and no discrimination occurs.

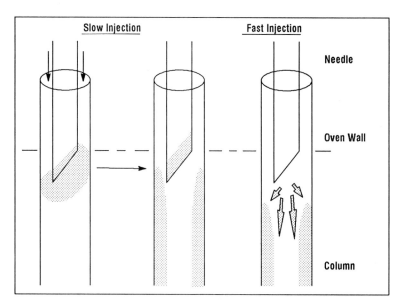

Figure 3-27. This diagram shows that by rapidly injecting the sample, the possibility of sample "coating" the outside of the needle is eliminated. The sample is condensed on the column at a point well away from the needle.

In most on-column systems, there is leakage during injection. This leak (carrier gas split) does not cause loss of sample material as long as the sample volume does not exceed 2 µl. The mobile phase, helium or hydrogen at velocities of 30–60 cm/sec, completely carries the sample into the column. If such problems are encountered, they are caused by a drastic pressure drop during injection; the carrier gas flow rate is reduced to such a level that back flow is observed. Remedies include installing a more effective restrictor or working with a continuous purge flow.

The oven temperature in on-column injection may be much higher than in splitless injection. In splitless injection, the solvent has to recondense. In on-column injections, on the other hand, the liquid is directly introduced into the column. Various studies have shown that, under normal operating conditions, (i.e., oven temperatures at or below the boiling point of the solvent) the sample liquid flows from the inlet section toward the rear of the column under the influence of the carrier gas. Upon injection in the column inlet, solvent and solutes spread over a certain distance until a stable solvent film is formed by the carrier gas flow. It is important to reduce the length of this flooded zone, because the solutes are distributed over its entire distance. The width of the initial band equals the length of the flooded zone (i.e., band broadening in space). (Band broadening in time, of course, does not occur in on-column injection). As discussed earlier, band broadening in space causes peak broadening and even peak splitting. The length of the flooded zone is a function of the column diameter, the volume injected, the actual inlet temperature, the stationary phase thickness, and (most important) the affinity of the solvent for the stationary phase.

For perfect wettability (i.e., apolar solvents on apolar silicone phases) the length of the flooded zone should be approximately 20 cm/µl injected. This length can be easily increased by a factor of ten or twenty if the wettability is poor, as is demonstrated by methanol injections on apolar silicone phases.

If the solutes are not refocused, band broadening in space makes qualitative and quantitative analyses impossible in cases when large sample volumes are injected or if the solvent does not wet the stationary phase properly. Figure 3-28 shows the peak profile of dodecane as a function of the sample volume. There is no difference in band width between 0.5 μl and 1.0 μl injections. For 2 μl samples, a contribution to the total peak variance is noticed; however, the peak is not distorted or split. On the other hand, distorted and split peak profiles are observed for injection volumes exceeding 2 μl.

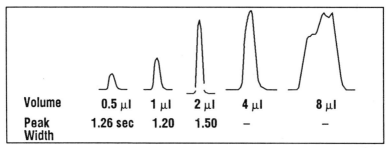

Volume	0.5 μl	1 μl	2 μl	4 μl	8 μl
Peak Width	1.26 sec	1.20	1.50	–	–

Figure 3-28. Peak width as a function of injection volume. The solute is dodecane and the solvent hexane. Column: 25 m x 0.31 mm SE-54. Hydrogen carrier gas at 44 cm/sec. Oven profile: 60° to 320°C at 15°C/min.

When 1 μl of a methanol solution is injected on an apolar column, solutes eluting at temperatures of 50–60°C above the boiling point of the solvent elute as split, distorted peaks. The analysis of a fraction collected from a step-elution HPLC analysis of the essential oil of L. Valeriana celtica with n-hexane and methanol illustrates this problem (Figure 3-29). The fraction of polar compounds was contained in 1 ml of n-hexane and 6 ml of methanol in a two-phase system. Both phases were injected on-column (1 μl) onto a 20 m x 0.3 mm id OV-1 column with a film thickness of 0.3 mm. Figure 3-29A shows the chromatogram of the methanol layer and Figure 3-29B that of the n-hexane layer. Methanol causes peak splitting, whereas n-hexane does not (48).

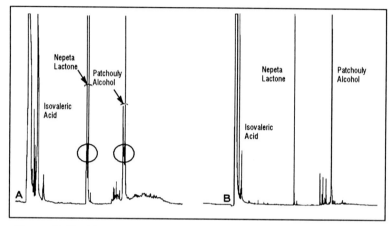

Figure 3-29. Chromatogram of fraction of the essential oil of
L.Valeriana celtica 1 μl injected on-column, Solvent A:
methanol, Solvent B: n-hexane. From Reference 48,
with permission of Elsevier, Amsterdam.

Poor wettability (polar-apolar) results in a long, unhomo-
geneous flooded zone. This can be circumvented via a
retention gap or by carrying out the analysis on a polar column
of the polyethylene glycol type. For a better understanding of
these phenomena, a visual representation of on-column
injection, carried out at an initial column temperature at or
below the boiling point of the solvent, is shown in Figure 3-30.
The sample is distributed over the flooded zone (A). As the
solvent evaporates, the more volatile components begin to
concentrate in the solvent (B,C). This evaporation process
starts at the inlet end of the column. Less volatile components
are distributed in the stationary phase. As the process
continues (C), two observations can be made. Volatile
material is reconcentrated by solvent trapping (small initial
band width), while less volatile compounds are distributed over
the length of the initially created flooded zone. Clearly, the
initial band width is directly related to the length of column over
which the sample is distributed. In fact, in comparison to split
injection, cold on-column always gives lower chromatographic
efficiencies if the inlet section of the column is coated.

Moreover, the distribution of the solutes in the flooded zone is far from homogeneous. High solute concentrations are located in the front and the rear of the flooded zone (49). If the flooded zone length is short (1 μl injections—good wettability), solutes recombine during the chromatographic process, but the chromatographic band will be broadened by 5% to 8% (48). If the flooded zone is too long (large injections—poor wettability), recombination during the chromatographic process is impossible and split/distorted peaks are generated. Focusing or reconcentration can be effected by applying a retention gap as shown in Figure 3-30D where the solute bands are narrowed by stationary phase focusing.

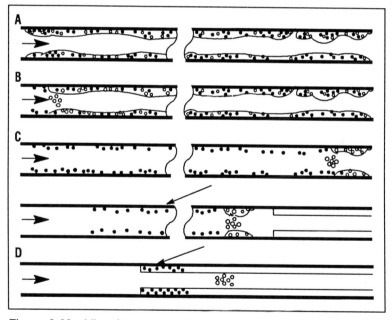

Figure 3-30. Visual representation of on-column injection.

Band broadening in space can be neglected for most applications. The enormous benefits of the technique largely overrule the loss in chromatographic efficiency for sample sizes of 1 μl. For large sample volumes, and when injecting polar solvents, the connection of a retention gap is recommended. The length of the retention gap should be 50–100 cm per microliter injected.

If properly performed, on-column injection provides the most accurate and precise results. Syringe discrimination, which is one of the main sources of error in the quantitative analysis of samples covering a wide range of molecular weights, is completely eliminated. Moreover, inlet-related discrimination does not occur, since the liquid is directly introduced onto the column. The analysis of a quantitative blend of hydrocarbons, ranging from C_8 to C_{40} in hexane, is shown in Figure 3-31.

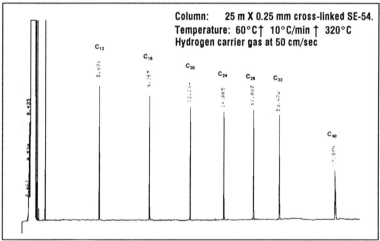

Figure 3-31. Representative chromatogram of C_8–C_{40} test blend.

The injection in Figure 3-31 was performed at 60°C, which is below the boiling point of the solvent. The solvent effect nicely concentrates C_8, while band broadening in space for C_{12} to C_{40} is negligible. Analytical precision (n=6) at two different concentrations is illustrated in Table 3-1.

Table 3-1.   Analytical Precision for a Series of Hydrocarbons at
Two Different Concentrations.

	14 ng (n=6) Area	% SD	≈140 pg (n=6) Area	% SD
C_8	288.20	0.76	5.15	2.90
C_{12}	309.09	0.49	3.16	1.57
C_{16}	306.65	0.47	3.03	1.63
C_{20}	287.12	0.70	3.05	1.27
C_{24}	274.21	0.57	2.95	2.54
C_{28}	289.83	0.58	3.12	0.80
C_{32}	282.86	0.58	3.21	0.59
C_{40}	264.46	0.51	2.93	0.79

The percent relative deviation at 14 ng is below 1%. At 0.14 ng
the precision is below 3%. The accuracy is outstanding as well.
All response factors for high boiling hydrocarbons in cold
on-column injection were calculated to be close to one. The
analysis of triglycerides, which are less inert and less
thermostable than hydrocarbons, is illustrated in Figure 3-32;
0.2 µl of a 0.05% hexane solution of a cocoa butter with low
polyunsaturated triglyceride content is introduced via a
movable on-column injector, with the oven temperature at
340°C. After elution of the solvent, the column inlet zone is
introduced in the oven and recording is started. The analytical
precision for the main triglycerides (POP, POS, and SOS) is
below 1% (50). Automated on-column injection provides even
higher analytical precision.

Figure 3-33 shows the analysis of a reference fatty acid methyl
ester mixture for microbial identification. The retention times
have a relative standard deviation between 0.02% to 0.05%
(n=11), and the peak area repeatability ranges from 0.06% to
0.6% RSD. The average deviation from the true value is less
than 1%, as shown in Table 3-2 (45).

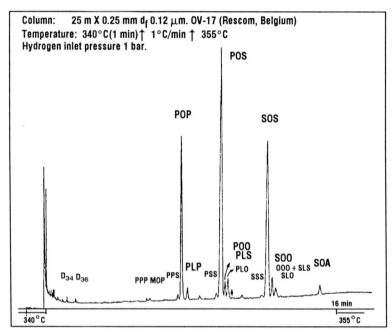

Figure 3-32. Capillary GC profile of cocoa butter with low content of polyunsaturated triglycerides. (Reproduced with permission from Reference 50. Copyright JAOCS.)

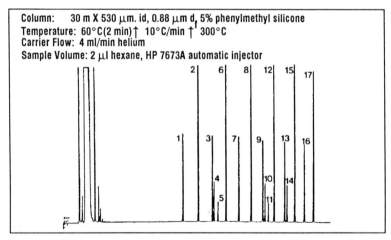

Figure 3-33. Chromatogram of straight chain saturated FAMES.

Table 3-2.   Accuracy of FAME Determination.

Chain Carbon #		Actual Weight	Mean (Raw) Area%	RRF	Mean (Corrected) Area%	Cor Area%/ Act Wt%
			Accuracy (Exp n = 11)			
9:0		4.99	4.89	1.02	4.99	1.00
10:0		10.02	10.02	1.00	10.02	1.00
11:0		5.01	5.00	1.00	5.00	1.00
10:0	αOH	2.50	2.26	1.10	2.49	0.99
10:0	βOH	1.26	1.17	1.08	1.26	1.00
12:0		10:00	10.16	1.00	10.16	1.02
13:0		5.00	4.96	1.00	4.96	0.99
14:0		10.00	10.19	0.98	9.99	1.00
15:0		4.99	5.05	0.99	5.00	1.00
14.0	αOH	2.51	2.33	1.05	2.45	0.97
14:0	βOH	1.25	1.17	1.07	1.25	1.00
16:0		10:00	10.23	0.98	10.03	1.00
17:0		5.00	5.00	0.97	4.87	0.97
16:0	αOH	2.50	2.29	1.09	2.50	1.00
18:0		9.98	10.16	0.99	10.06	1.01
19:0		4.99	5.03	0.97	4.88	0.98
20:0		9.99	10.10	0.99	10.00	1.00

The Relative Response Factors are for illustration and are not intended for use as a replacement for normal instrument calibration procedures.

The automated on-column analysis of free fatty acids, from acetic acid to decanoic acid, is shown in Figure 3-34 (51). Relative standard deviations on absolute peak areas were below 1%, and on relative peak areas below 0.4% for twenty injections (n=20). The injection temperature in this case was 20°C above the boiling point of the solvent (dichloromethane). In this example, peak broadening and distortion was avoided by applying secondary cooling. Supplementary cooling can be very advantageous in routine analysis. However, cooling down the oven to temperatures below or at the boiling point of the solvent can be very time-consuming.

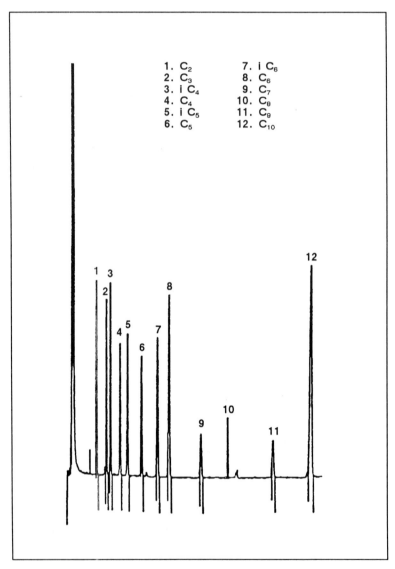

Figure 3-34. Free fatty acids on a wide bore column. (Reproduced with permission from Reference 51, Copyright Elsevier, Amsterdam.)

Figure 3-35 shows chromatograms of piperine, the single pungent principle of peppers and pepper extracts (52). One-half microliter of dichloromethane solution was injected quickly at an oven temperature of 100°C with supplementary cooling of the first centimeters of the column.

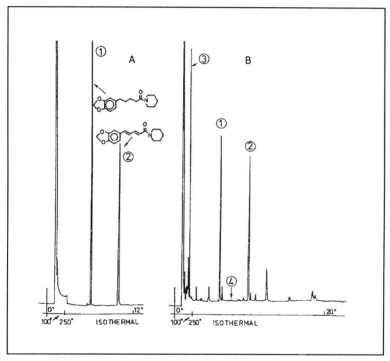

Figure 3-35. Glass capillary GC analysis with cold on-column injection of (A) pure piperine and (B) a black pepper extract. Internal standard (peak 1) is tetrahydro-piperine; peak 2 is piperine. Column: 25 m x 0.5 mm id HTS-OV-1 column, 250°C isothermal; carrier gas (hydrogen) flow rate, 4.6 ml/min. (Reproduced with permission from Reference 52, Copyright Elsevier, Amsterdam.)

After introduction of the sample, the column temperature was immediately raised to 250°C. The high boiling solutes are focused properly in the first few centimeters of the column, while the solvent evaporates from the front to the rear. Back flow did not occur by a combined effect of supplementary cooling, small sample volume, and large internal diameter column. The relative standard deviation for replicate analysis (n=6) of both standards (A) and samples (B) is 1.0%. This is superior to what could be achieved by HPLC. The data presented indicates that both the external standard and the internal standard method can be applied for quantitation.

Current literature data contain overwhelming evidence for the superior features of cold on-column injection in quantitative work. A second important feature of cold on-column injection is the elimination of sample alterations. Thermally labile components are not exposed to thermal stress; they begin the chromatographic process at relatively low temperatures. Decomposition and rearrangement reactions are almost completely eliminated. This permits analyses which heretofore were impossible with gas chromatography. The Grobs demonstrated this very clearly (30). The quantitative analysis of mustard oils and a related nitrile present in radishes was only possible when cold on-column injection was used.

Figure 3-36 shows the analysis of some underivatized mycotoxins in the nanogram range. The absence of compound alteration was evidenced by CGC-MS illustrating its compatibility with cold on-column injection. Figure 3-37 shows the total ion trace of silylated aromatic hydroxy acids. Due to the low stability of these TMS derivatives, cold on-column injection was the method of choice.

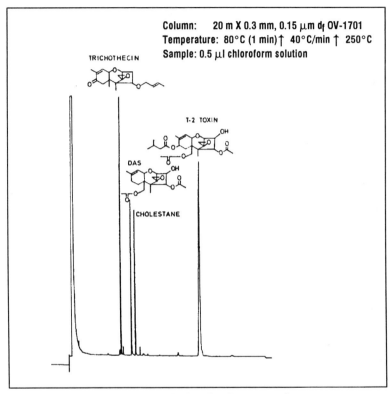

Figure 3-36. Analysis of underivatized mycotoxins.

Disadvantages of On-Column Injection

In comparison to vaporizing injectors, there are a number of disadvantages to cold on-column sampling that should be mentioned. Since the sample is introduced directly onto the column, relatively "clean" samples must be prepared. Involatile and less volatile material collects at the head of the column. The presence of this material causes a loss of separation efficiency and can introduce adsorptive sites in the column inlet. Therefore, proper sample cleanup is very important. When dirty samples are unavoidable, the use of a precolumn (which can simultaneously act as a retention gap) is recommended.

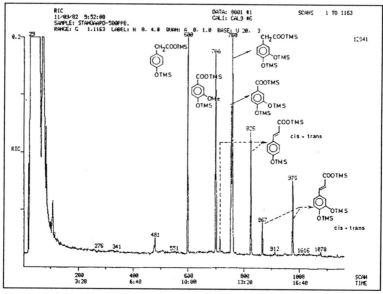

Figure 3-37. Silylated aromatic hydroxy acids.
Column: 25 m x 0.25 mm id d$_f$ 0.25 μm SE-54
Temperature: 60°C ↑ 8°C/min ↑ 200°C
Sample: 0.8 μl in n-hexane

With the advent of immobilized stationary phases, solvent rinsing of the column is possible and can effectively remove chemical contamination. In some cases, however, involatiles may be soluble and can migrate into the stationary phase film where they are fixed. Cutting off part of the column (20 cm to 50 cm) is the most effective remedy.

Real samples are often too concentrated for on-column injection, and have to be diluted. As simple as this may seem, this often creates undesired peaks. The sensitivity that can be reached with on-column injection is beyond 1 ppm. This means that solvent impurities in concentrations of milligrams per liter will disturb the sample profile. Even pure analysis solvents often contain impurities in this concentration range. Subtraction of blank runs of the solvent used for diluting samples is often required in practical work. Solvents can often be adequately purified by solid phase extraction, followed by distillation using a Vigreux or Sidward column.

A final drawback of cold on-column injection, which is not fully recognized, is the limited applicability of the technique to samples containing large amounts of individual components. Quantitative determination of solutes eluting before major compounds is impossible due to the fact that the high concentration compound acts like a solvent. This causes solutes to elute as distorted peaks because of partial solvent trapping (29). This phenomenon is also referred to as a reverse solvent effect. For this reason, the analysis of styrene monomers depicted in Figure 3-9 (split injection) is impossible using on-column injection. Due to the low concentration of impurities, dilution to the level required for avoiding peak distortion cannot be carried out. This phenomenon can be easily demonstrated. High concentrations of dioctylphthalate (DOP) are added to a sample with a wide range of volatile components, yielding satisfactory results with cold on-column injection. Upon repeating the analysis, peaks eluting before DOP will be distorted. This distortion is not reproducible over several injections. Depending on the polarity difference of the matrix solutes, different peak profiles can be observed. Components having similar polarity will result in strongly distorted peaks (fixation effect), while large polarity differences can yield normal peak profiles (exaltation effect). For such samples, improved results can be obtained by PTV (programmed temperature vaporizing) injection. Despite these shortcomings, cold on-column injection is currently the best injection method for most applications.

Guidelines for On-Column Injection

- Sample volumes between 0.5 μl and 2 μl are injected rapidly at oven temperatures equal to or below the boiling point of the solvent. If supplementary inlet cooling is used, the oven temperature can be above the boiling point of the solvent.

- After injection, the liquid is allowed to form a stable film (flooded zone). This takes several seconds. If the solutes to be analyzed differ much in boiling points in comparison to the solvent, ballistic heating to high temperature is allowed. On the other hand, if the solute boiling points do not differ too much compared to the solvent, temperature pro-gramming is applied to fully exploit the solvent effect.

- When peak splitting and/or peak distortion is observed, the connection of a retention gap can provide the solution.

- For quantitation, both the internal standard and the external standard methods can be applied.

- If the composition of the sample is not that complex, the use of wide bore columns should be considered, particularly since automated injection becomes easier. If high resolution is needed with automated injection, a deactivated but uncoated wide bore precolumn (20 cm to 50 cm in length) should be connected to the analytical narrow bore column.

- Hydrogen is the carrier gas of choice. If H_2 cannot be used for safety reasons, helium may be substituted. High carrier gas velocities (50–80 cm/sec H_2, 30–50 cm/sec He) guarantee negligible band broadening.

Direct Injection

Because injection techniques are named as they are developed, and terms which originally meant one thing now mean something else, some misnomers have resulted. Direct injection is an example of such a misnomer. Direct injection is often confused or even identified with on-column injection. The understanding of this terminology as discussed in this book and based upon the chronological order in which techniques were developed, is as follows:

– *Direct Injection* is a flash vaporizing injection method. The inlet system is heated separately and independently from the column oven, and evaporation occurs in the inlet. This inlet can be a glass liner (out-column evaporation) or a part of the column (in-column evaporation). Injection peak broadening is caused by broadening in time and broadening in space. Different direct injection devices are shown in Figure 3-38.

– *On-column Injection* is a "cold" injection technique. The sample is injected as a liquid directly onto the column. During injection, the injection zone is cooled to avoid hot needle discrimination. Injection peak broadening is caused only by broadening in space. The solutes are focused in the inlet section of the column, from where evaporation gradually starts as the oven temperature is raised. On-column injection can be applied for all conventional capillary columns (0.25 mm, 0.32 mm, and 0.53 mm id), but direct injection is restricted to use with wide bore or megabore columns.

Direct injection into wide bore columns was first described in 1959 (53). At that time, column efficiency was all important. The quantitative aspect of direct injection, however, has never really been studied in depth. Through the introduction of wide bore fused silica capillary columns with an id of 0.53 mm, the interest in direct sampling has been renewed. Injection on a 0.53 mm id FSOT column, operated in the high resolution mode (flow rates 2 to 5 ml/min) or in the low-resolution mode (flow rates 5 to 20 ml/min) as a packed column alternative is advertised to be as easy as installing a simple glass liner in the packed column inlet and connecting the column to it (54). This view is slightly oversimplified. Since the direct injection technique is based on the evaporation of the sample at elevated injection temperatures, all previous statements about syringe discrimination and band broadening effects remain

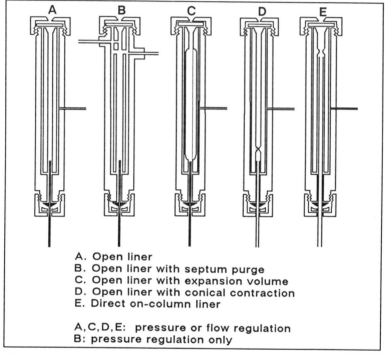

A. Open liner
B. Open liner with septum purge
C. Open liner with expansion volume
D. Open liner with conical contraction
E. Direct on-column liner

A,C,D,E: pressure or flow regulation
B: pressure regulation only

Figure 3-38. Glass liners for direct injection.

valid. For direct injection to produce optimal results, contributing factors must be carefully determined. Unfortunately, a thorough study has not yet been completed for direct injection into 0.53 mm columns. Such an evaluation would surely demonstrate the poor performance of several inserts presently in use. Despite this lack of a systematic study, some experience-based guidelines on direct injection into wide bore columns are discussed. It should be noted that wide bore capillary columns can be effectively coupled to any type of capillary injector (split, splitless, on-column, programmed temperature vaporization). When megabore columns are used in the high resolution mode (i.e., at flow rates close to the optimum) the same general guidelines as for narrow bore columns apply.

For normal sample sizes (i.e., samples of approximately 1 μl), direct injection compares very well to splitless injection. The same operational criteria can be followed:

– For manual injections, the fast hot-needle injection technique is preferred to minimize syringe discrimination.

– For quantitative work, syringe discrimination is inherent in all vaporizing injectors; in this respect, direct injection is no exception.

– To avoid sample losses due to overfilling the insert with sample vapors, the point of injection should be close to the column entrance.

– Long and narrow inserts are preferred to minimize sample dilution (band broadening in time).

– Band broadening should be compensated for by refocusing the solutes in the inlet section of the column. The principles of solvent effect and of thermal focusing were discussed previously.

– Injections of microliter volumes at oven temperatures far above the boiling point of the solvent should be avoided, unless the sample is known to contain only heavy compounds which will be refocused by cold trapping at the chosen column temperature.

One disadvantage of direct injection in comparison to splitless injection is that it lacks inlet purge and septum purge facilities. A consequence of this is large, tailing solvent peaks and the occurrence of ghost peaks. The advent of the septum purge systems for direct injection has resolved the problem of ghost peaks (Figure 3-38B). Solvent peak tailing can be reduced drastically by increasing the septum purge flow for 10 seconds (to purge the inlet) after allowing the carrier gas to sweep the injector for 20–30 seconds.

The high speed of injection, which is advocated in direct injection, at first sight might seem surprising (51). It can be shown that a slow injection (1-2 seconds) results in much better solvent peak shapes, especially when using large volume glass liners (Figure 3-38C). However, despite the better solvent peak shape, syringe discrimination increases. The temperature difference between the injection port and the boiling point of the solvent is of utmost importance. The injection speed (fast-slow), the boiling point and the nature of the solvent, the injector temperature, and the oven temperature must be tuned for each application which uses direct injection.

Quantitation in direct injection can also be hampered by peak broadening in time and in space. The use of the aforementioned techniques, the solvent effect and cold trapping, can suppress these phenomena. This is illustrated in Figure 3-39, which shows the analysis of environmental pollutant standards on a thick film column.

Components 2 to 57 in Figure 3-39 elute with perfect peak shapes through refocusing by cold trapping at the initial column temperature of 40°C. This effect is facilitated by the large film thickness. In temperature programmed runs, peak broadening is less problematic because cold trapping automatically occurs. Moreover, wide bore columns (per definition) yield wider peaks so that injection contributions to the peak variance become less important.

Small injection volumes of approximately 0.2 µl to 0.3 µl are frequently used in direct injection at elevated temperatures. Plunger-in-needle syringes (1 µl) are very useful for controlling such small sample volumes. In this case, direct on-column injection can be applied onto wide bore columns (Figure 3-38E). To avoid stationary phase stripping by the syringe needle, the stationary phase should be washed from the inlet section of the capillary column. For columns with immobilized films, connecting a capillary precolumn or a

Column: 30 m X 530 μm id, 1.5 μm Rtx
Temperature: 40°C(6 min)↑ 10°C/min ↑ 300°C (15 min)
Injector and Detector temp: 300°C
Carrier gas: hydrogen at 80 cm/sec
Sample volume: 2.5 μl inlet design type C (Fig 38)

1. N-Nitrosodimethylamine
2. Phenol
3. 2-Chlorophenol
4. bis(2-Chloroethyl)ether
5. 1,3-Dichlorobenzene
6. 1,4-Dichlorobenzene
7. 1,2-Dichlorobenzene
8. bis(2-Chloroisopropyl) ether
9. Hexachloroethane
10. N-Nitroso-di-n-propylamine
11. Nitrobenzene
12. Isophorone
13. 2-Nitrophenol
14. 2,4-Dimethylphenol
15. bis(2-Chloroethoxy)methane
16. 2,4-dichlorophenol
17. 1,2,4-Trichlorobenzene
18. Naphthalene
19. Hexachlorobutadiene
20. p-Chloro-m-cresol
21. Hexachlorocyclopentadiene
22. 2,4,6-Trichlorophenol
23. 2-Chloronaphthalene
24. Acenaphthylene
25. Dimethyl phthalate
26. 2,6-Dinitrotoluene
27. Acenaphthene
28. 2,4-Dinitrophenol
29. 4-Nitrophenol

30. 2,4-dinitrotoluene
31. Diethyl phthalate
32. Fluorene
33. 4-Chlorophenylphenyl ether
34. 4,6-dinitro-o-cresol
35. N-Nitrosodiphenylamine
36. 1,2-Diphenyl hydrazine
37. 4-Bromophenylether
38. Hexachlorobenzene
39. Pentachlorophenol
40. Phenanthrene
41. Anthracene
42. Di-n-butyl phthalate
43. Fluoranthene
44. Benzidine
45. Pyrene
46. Butylbenzyl phthalate
47. Benzo(a)anthracene
48. 3,3'-Dichlorobenzidine
49. Chrysene
50. bis(2-Ethylhexyl)phthalate
51. Di-n-octyl phthalate
52. Benzo(b)fluoranthene
53. Benzo(k)fluoranthene
54. Benzo(a)pyrene
55. Indeno(1,2,3-ccd)pyrene
56. Dibenzo(a,h)anthracene
57. Benzo(ghi)perylene

Figure 3-39. Analysis of environmental compounds (continued on
            next page).

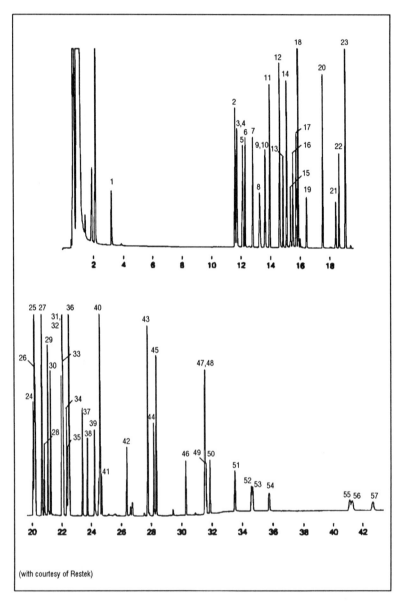

(with courtesy of Restek)

Figure 3-39. Analysis of environmental compounds (continued from previous page).

deactivated retention gap can provide the solution. Figure 3-40 shows the analysis of the oxygenated fraction of hop oil dissolved in dichloromethane on a narrow bore column using split injection and on a wide bore column using direct injection (55). Both columns (25 m x 0.25 mm and 50 m x 0.50 mm) offer the same efficiency. Peak broadening did not occur in Figure 3-40B, for which only 0.2 μl was injected. Syringe discrimination occurs in both the split and the direct injection analyses.

Syringe discrimination can be eliminated by using an automated fast injection process to reduce the needle dwell time in the injection port. Figure 3-41 shows the effect of the needle dwell time for 1 μl n-hexane and 1 μl n-pentane injections of hydrocarbons. Peak area ratios C_x/C_{20} (x=10 to 40) are plotted for different dwell times. The needle dwell time is defined as the time interval between the needle piercing the bottom of the septum on the way in and reaching the same point on the way out. For the n-hexane solution, injected at 350°C on an injection port packed with glass wool, discrimination is nearly absent at a dwell time of 500 ms. The n-pentane solution, however, requires a dwell time as short as 250 ms for obtaining the same result. This clearly illustrates the importance of the solvent boiling point; the more volatile the solvent, the faster distillation out of the needle will occur. A study on the performance of direct injection inlets was presented at the 9th International Symposium on Capillary Chromatography, May 1988, in Monterey, California, USA (55).

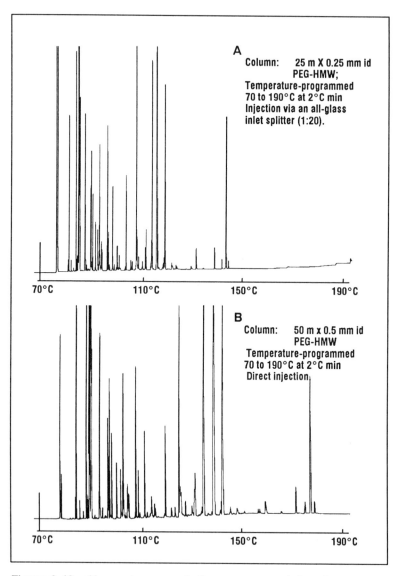

Figure 3-40. Chromatogram of the oxygenated fraction of hop essential oil on a narrowbore (A) and widebore (B) capillary.

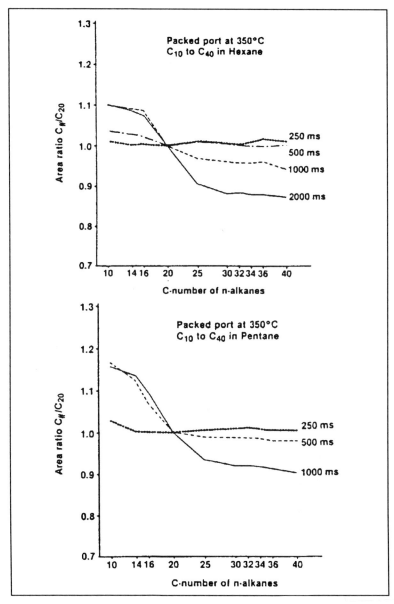

Figure 3-41. Effect of needle dwell time in the injection port on fractionation.

Programmed Temperature Vaporizing (PTV) Injection

In 1979, Vogt and coworkers (56,57) described an injection method for the introduction of sample volumes up to 250 μl. The sample was slowly introduced into a cold glass insert packed with glass wool. The low-boiling solvent was continuously evaporated and vented through the split exit. The solutes, which remained in the inlet, were transferred to the capillary column by rapidly heating (30°C/min) the inlet. During this transfer, the split line was closed (splitless injection).

Based on this idea, two groups [Schomburg et al. (58,60) and Poy et al. (59,61)] almost simultaneously developed pro-grammed temperature injection techniques. Their aim, however, was not the injection of large sample volumes but rather the elimination of syringe needle discrimination, which at that time was the subject of interest. Several groups further developed PTV injection, often called cold split-splitless injection. Different PTV injection devices are commercially available, offering a broad range of possibilities, (i.e., hot or cold split injection, hot or cold splitless injection, cold on-column injection, direct injection, etc.). Through these possibilities used in association with the available injection methods and devices, and techniques such as the injection of large sample volumes, concentration by multiple injection, solvent venting, etc., PTV injection is claimed to be the most universal sample introduction system. It is not the answer for all applications, however. Moreover, the performances of PTV injection have not yet been fully explored. More practical data are needed to formulate final conclusions. The different configurations will not be discussed here, but the operational principle of the cold split-splitless method will be outlined.

Figure 3-42 shows a schematic of a PTV injection system. The system consists of a 5 cm to 8 cm long glass liner, with an od of 0.2 cm and an id of 0.1 cm, packed with silanized glass wool. The insert is sealed against the metal body and prevents carrier gas from entering from the bottom. The capillary column penetrates 0.5 to 0.8 cm into the liner.

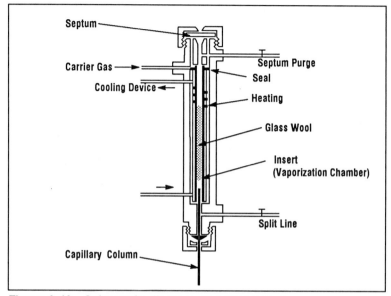

Figure 3-42. Schematic diagram of a PTV-injector.

The upper part of the PTV inlet resembles a classical split-splitless device, including carrier gas inlet and septum flush. Septum-free devices have also been developed (62,63). Whatever the construction, the upper part of the inlet always remains cold. The sample is injected into the glass liner while the injector body is cold. After withdrawal of the syringe needle, the vaporizing tube is heated rapidly to vaporize the solvent and the solutes. The heat can be provided electrically (see Figure 3-42) or by means of preheated compressed air. Depending on the construction of the devices, heating of the device can be performed ballistically (58,59) or linearly at selected heat-up rates (for example 2°C to 12°C/second) and to consecutive temperature levels (63). These facilities permit special handling such as: the optimization of conditions for the analysis of thermally labile compounds, operating in the solvent vent mode when working with specific detection such as ECD or mass spectrometry, concentration through multiple injections, etc. Split or splitless injection can be achieved through regulation of the split valve. During or after the chromatographic run, the vaporizing chamber is cooled by air or carbon dioxide, in preparation for the next injection. Cooling down takes 1 to 5 minutes. The three most important modes of operation, cold split injection, solvent elimination injection, and cold splitless injection, are discussed briefly.

Cold Split Injection

In cold split injection, the liquid plug is introduced into a cold vaporizing chamber. This prevents sample evaporation inside the syringe needle. Two important consequences are that syringe fractionation does not occur and the introduced sample volume can be measured more accurately than in classical split injection. Quantitation by the external standard method thus becomes more accurate. The internal volume of the vaporizing chamber is kept small to constitute a low thermal mass and allow rapid heating and cooling. Care must be taken not to overfill the insert with sample vapors. Relatively high split ratios and low sample volumes are recommended. Large volumes can be introduced if the evaporation of the solvent is started before heating the injector. This can be achieved by selecting solvents with low boiling points, high split ratios, and/or using an initial injection temperature near the boiling point of the solvent. On the other hand, vaporization of heavy components is rather slow. To avoid band broadening, thermal focusing of the solute bands by oven-programmed temperature mode is often needed.

Solvent Elimination Injection

For solvent elimination injection, the sample is introduced into the cold injector with the split valve open. The conditions are selected to permit only the solvent to evaporate. The solvent vapors are vented through the split line. After completion of solvent evaporation, the split line remains open (solvent elimination split mode) or is closed (solvent elimination splitless mode). The last mode is most frequently applied. The solutes are then transferred into the column by heating the injector. In this procedure, losses of volatile sample components cannot be avoided. The applicability of the technique is restricted, therefore, to the analysis of heavy compounds; and large sample volumes can be introduced by applying slow injection. Trapping of medium volatiles can be enhanced by packing the insert with adsorbents such as Tenax, active charcoal, Chromosorb, etc. Excellent retention can be obtained, but the desorption temperatures required are very high (300–350°C). Also, decomposition has been observed for polar compounds (64).

Solvent venting is also applied in multiple injection (63). Figure 3-43 shows the chromatogram obtained after eight injections of 1 µl of a mixture of C_{13} to C_{20} in hexane (concentration 5 ppm). The solvent was vented after the last injection. Under the conditions applied, C_{13} to C_{16} are discriminated through co-venting with the solvent. No discrimination is observed from C_{17} to C_{20}.

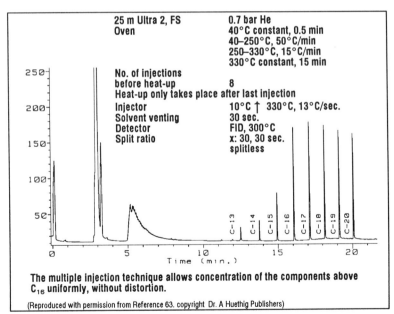

Figure 3-43. Example of multiple injection.

Cold Splitless Injection

As in conventional splitless injection, in cold splitless injection the split exit is closed during injection of the sample. In contrast, however, the vaporizing chamber is cold, preventing discrimination inside the syringe needle. The injector is then heated and the sample transferred into the column, the temperature of which is maintained far below the boiling point of the solvent to reconcentrate the solute bands by the solvent effect. After a preselected time (30 to 90 seconds), the split line is activated to vent residual vapors from the glass liner. Due to the small volume of the glass liner, small sample volumes (<1 µl) are usually injected to avoid overflow of the injector. The analysis of coal tar with cold splitless injection is shown in Figure 3-44 (65) using both cold splitless (A) and cold split (B) injection. For larger sample volumes, it is recommended that solvent evaporation be initiated before heating the injector. This can be done either by selecting a solvent with a low boiling point or by using an elevated starting injection temperature.

Quantitative data obtained by PTV splitless injection and cold on-column injection have been compared (65,66). Table 3-3 shows the results of a test for discrimination. Relative normalized peak areas of C_{10} to C_{32} were determined. For that particular case, splitless PTV injection performs excellently. On the other hand, it has been shown that cold splitless injection cannot be applied for simulated distillation (paraffins as high as C_{120}) (67).

Problems with PTV injection can be encountered with labile compounds. Saravalle et al. (62) reported decomposition of trimethylsilyl esters of fatty acids (Donike-test) with cold splitless injection, while cold on-column and cold split injection did not show deterioration. In cold splitless injection the residence time of the compounds in the liner is long, causing

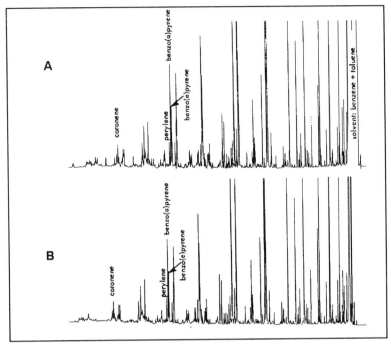

Figure 3-44. The analysis of coal tar with PTV injection in the splitless and split modes. (A) Cold (TP) injection in splitless mode: Sampling of components of very low volatility [polyaromatic hydrocarbons of coal tar (highly diluted) in benzene]. Sample: 0.4 µl of coal tar. Column: 20 m methylpolysiloxane OV-1 on fused silica. Column temperatures: 1 min isothermal at 25°C, ballistic heating from 25 to 80°C, then from 80 to 320°C at 8°C/min; Injector, 35–280°C ballistic heating. Carrier gas: 0.4 bar hydrogen. Analysis time: 35 min. (B) Cold (TP) injection in split mode: sampling of components of very low volatility [polyaromatic hydrocarbons of coal tar (less diluted) in toluene]. Sample: 0.2 µl of coal tar diluted in toluene. Column: 20 m methylpolysiloxane OV-1 on fused silica. Column temperatures: from 25 to 80°C with ballistic heating, from 80 to 320°C at 8°C/min; injector 25–280°C ballistic heating. Carrier gas: 0.4 bar hydrogen. Analysis time: 35 min. (Reproduced with permission from Reference 66. Copyright Elsevier, Amsterdam.)

decomposition by thermal stress or by activity of the glass wool. For several applications the inertness, even of well deactivated glass wool, is not good enough. To overcome these problems, unpacked liners (Figure 3-45) with deformation of the cross-section have been introduced (68).

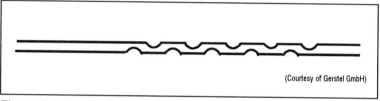

(Courtesy of Gerstel GmbH)

Figure 3-45. PTV—inlet tube with deformation of the cross-section.

In conclusion, programmed-temperature vaporizing injection is a promising technique. Excellent results have been achieved; more investigation, however, is necessary to establish the applicability of this technique. The power of the technique lies mainly in the possibility of "programming" the injection port. In this respect, devices using ballistic heating are not PTV injectors and do not offer the same possibilities as do linearly heated devices with programmable temperature rates and different consecutive temperature levels.

Table 3-3.   Discrimination Tests Using the Cold On-column and
Splitless Cold (TP) Injection Techniques.
Determination of Relative (Normalized) Peak Areas
of C_{10}–C_{32} Paraffins.

	A "Cold (on-column)"* Peak Area %	% s.d.	B "Cold TP" (splitless)* Peak Area %	% s.d.
C_{10}	8.18	0.38	8.26	0.46
C_{12}	8.26	0.34	8.37	0.31
C_{14}	8.21	0.44	8.27	0.30
C_{16}	8.29	0.55	8.23	0.41
C_{18}	8.44	0.66	8.26	0.48
C_{20}	8.53	0.88	8.22	0.30
C_{22}	8.31	0.29	8.52	0.47
C_{24}	8.24	0.52	8.39	0.45
C_{26}	8.26	0.55	8.62	0.69
C_{28}	8.42	0.72	8.39	0.58
C_{30}	8.42	0.69	8.29	0.33
C_{32}	8.42	0.71	8.16	0.46
Sample:	0.2 µl C_{10}–C_{32} in C7, 0.002 % each comp		0.4 ml C_{10}–C_{32} in C_7, 0.002% each comp	
Column:	24 m OV 101		24 m OV 101	
Temps:	2' iso 50–300°C, 15°C/min		1' iso 50–300°C, 15°C/min Inj:35–300°C	
Carrier gas:	0.45 bar H_2		0.58 bar He	

*Number of Measurements: 7

References

1. Pretorius, V., and W. Bertsch. 1983. *HRC & CC* 6:64.

2. Jenkins, R., and W. Jennings. 1983. *HRC & CC* 6:228.

3. Sandra, P. 1985. *Sample Introduction in Capillary Gas Chromatography* Vol 1. Heidelberg: Dr. A. Huethig.

4. Grob, K. 1986. *Classical Split and Splitless Injection in Capillary GC.* Heidelberg: Dr. A. Huethig.

5. Grob, K. 1987. *On-Column Injection in Capillary GC.* Heidelberg: Dr. A. Huethig.

6. Sandra, P. in preparation. *Sample Introduction in Capillary Gas Chromatography* Vol 2. Heidelberg: Dr. A. Huethig.

7. Desty, R., A. Goldup, and H. Whyman. 1959. *J Inst Petroleum* 45:287.

8. Smith, D., P. Bente III, R. Freeman, and J. Cusack. *Hewlett-Packard Technical Paper No. 74.*

9. Schomburg, G., H. Husmann and F. Weeke. 1975. *J Chromatogr* 112:205.

10. Kugler, E., W. Halang, R. Schlenkermann, H. Webel, and E. Langlais. 1977. *Chromatographia* 10:438.

11. Neu, H. 1987. *Proc 8th Int Symp Capillary Chromatography, Riva del Garda, Italy* pp 142. Heidelberg: Dr. A. Huethig.

12. Phillips, R., R. Wolstromer, and R. Freeman, *Hewlett-Packard Application Note AN 228-16.*

13. Grob Jr, K., and H. Neukom. 1979. *HRC & CC* 2:15.

14. Grob Jr, K., and H. Neukom. 1980. *HRC & CC* 3:627.

15. Grob, K., and G. Grob. 1979. *HRC & CC* 2:109.

16. Schomburg, G., U. Hausig, H. Husmann, and H. Behlau. 1984. *Chromatographia* 19:29.

17. Snyder, W. D. *Hewlett-Packard Technical Paper No. 108.*

18. Schomburg, G., and U. Hausig. 1985. *HRC & CC* 8:572.

19. Proot, M., and P. Sandra. 1986. *HRC & CC* 9:619.

20. Proot, M., F. David, P. Sandra, and M. Verzele. 1985. *HRC & CC* 8:426.

21. Grob, K., and G. Grob. 1969. *J Chromatogr Sci* 7:584.

22. Grob, K., and G. Grob. 1969. *J Chromatogr Sci* 7:587.

23. Grob Jr, K. 1981. *J Chromatogr* 213:13.

24. Grob Jr, K. 1985. *J Chromatogr* 324:252.

25. Grob Jr, K. 1981. *J Chromatogr* 213:3.

26. Grob Jr, K. 1982. *J Chromatogr* 237:15.

27. Sandra, P., G. Redant, and B. Denoulet. Submitted 1988. *HRC & CC. in press.*

28. Rooney, T. A., *Hewlett-Packard Application Note AN 228-5.*

29. Grob Jr, K. 1982. *J Chromatogr* 251:235.

30. Grob, K., and K. Grob Jr. 1978. *J Chromatogr* 151:311.

31. Grob, K. 1978. *HRC & CC* 1:263.

32. Schomburg, G., H. Behlau, R. Dielmann, F. Weeke, and H. Hushman. 1977. *J Chromatogr* 142:87.

33. Galli, M., S. Trestianu, and K. Grob Jr. 1979. *HRC & CC* 2:366.

34. Galli, M., and S. Trestianu. 1981. *J Chromatogr* 203:193.

35. Hinshaw, J. V., and F. J. Yang.1983. *HRC & CC* 6:554.

36. Freeman, R. R., K. B. Augenblick, and R. J. Phillips. *Hewlett-Packard Technical Paper 88.*

37. Knauss, K., J. Fulleman and M. P. Turner. *Hewlett-Packard Technical Paper 94.*

38. Geeraert, E., P. Sandra, and D. De Schepper. 1983. *J Chromatogr* 279:287.

39. Geeraert, E., D. De Schepper, and P. Sandra. 1983. *HRC & CC* 6:386.

40. van den Berg, P. M. J., and T. Cox. 1972. *Chromatographia* 5:301.

41. Jennings, W. *J & W Catalogue.*

42. Termonia, M., F. Munari, and P. Sandra. 1987. *HRC & CC* 10:263.

43. Dawes, E. *SGE Catalogue.*

44. Badings, H. T., and C. de Jong. 1983. *J Chromatogr* 279:493.

45. Kolloff, R. H., C. Toney, and J. Butler. *Hewlett-Packard Technical Paper 110.*

46. Grob Jr., K., C. Walder, and B. Schilling. 1986. *HRC & CC* 9:95.

47. Grob Jr., K., and J. M. Stoll. 1986. *HRC & CC* 9:518.

48. Sandra, P., M. van Roelenbosch, M. Verzele, and C. Bicchi. 1983. *J Chromatogr* 279:279.

49. Grob Jr., K. 1981. *J Chromatogr* 213:3.

50. Geeraert, E., and P. Sandra. 1987. *JAOCS* Vol 64.1:100.

51. Sandra, P. 1985. The Science of Chromatography. *J Chromatogr, Library Vol 32.* pp 381.

52. Verzele, M., G. Redant, S. Qureshi, and P. Sandra. 1980. *J Chromatogr* 199:105.

53. Zlatkis, A., and H. R. Kaufman. 1959. *Nature* 184:4010.

54. In Restek, Halfmil Capillary Columns, Catalogue.

55. Turner, K., H. McNair, P. Sandra, and F. David. 1988. *9th Int Symp Cap Chromatography, Monterey* pp. 176. Heidelberg: Dr. A. Huethig.

56. Vogt, W.,   K. Jacob, and   H. W. Obwexer. 1979. *J Chromatogr* 174:437.

57. Vogt, W., K. Jacob, A. B. Ohnesorge, and H. W. Obwexer. 1979. *J Chromatogr* 186:197.

58. Schomburg, G. 1981. *4th Int Symp Cap Chromatography, Hindelang, W. Germany* pp. 921. Heidelberg: Dr. A. Huethig

59. Poy, F., S. Visani, and F. Terrosi. 1981. *J Chromatogr* 217:81.

60. Schomburg, G. 1985. *Sample Introduction in Capillary Gas Chromatography: Vol 1.* pp. 55 and references cited therein. Heidelberg:Dr. A. Huethig.

61. Poy, F., and L. Cobelli. 1985. *Sample Introduction in Capillary Gas Chromatography, Vol 1.* pp 77 and references cited therein. Heidelberg: Dr. A. Huethig.

62. Saravalle, C., F. Munari, and S. Trestianu. 1985. *Proc 6th Int Symp Capillary Chromatography, Riva del Garda, Italy* pp 227. Heidelberg: Dr. A. Huethig. also. 1987. *HRC & CC*, 10:288.

63. Lendero, L., E. Gerstel, and J. Gerstel. 1987. *Proc 8th Int Symp Capillary Chromatography,"* Riva del Garda, Italy pp 342. Heidelberg: Dr. A. Heuthig.

64. Sandra, P., unpublished results.

65. Schomburg, G., H. Husmann, H. Behlau, and F. Schulz. 1983. *J Chromatogr* 279:251.

66. Schomburg, G., H. Husmann, and F. Schulz. 1983. *J Chromatogr.* 279:259.

67. Saravalle, C., F. Munari, and S. Trestianu. 1987. *HRC & CC* 10:288.

68. Gerstel, E., *Cooled Injection Systems, Gerstel GmbH Catalogue.*

CHAPTER 4. INSTRUMENTATION

I. THE OVEN

K. J. Hyver

The quality of chromatography retention data depends on the reproducible performance of the gas chromatography system. Instrument contribution to variance in retention time is a summation of the variances in run initiation, system control, and data output.

$$\sigma_{t_R}^2 = \sigma_{\text{run initiation}}^2 + \sigma_{\text{system control}}^2 + \sigma_{\text{data output}}^2$$

Automated liquid sampling devices can significantly reduce the variance in run initiation. Variation due to the oven program initiation electronics is extremely small and reproducible (<0.005 minutes) and, therefore, insignificant. The variance from data output devices (electrometer, detector, integrator, etc.) can also be considered negligible. Therefore, the major source of error in the measurement of retention time is due to system control. There are two aspects of system control that significantly affect the reproducibility of chromatography data- pneumatic control and oven temperature control. Poorly designed pneumatic regulation can result in variance of the linear flow velocity through the column. The most stable column flow can be achieved with electronic forward pressure regulation.

Oven Temperature Control

Temperature gradients and random fluctuations cause variance in the partition ratio, k, which affects the repro- ducibility of chromatographic retention. Thermal control is especially critical for reliable retention data in capillary gas chromatography applications utilizing pattern recognition and retention time or retention index for qualitative identification.

An investigation of the effects of temperature variations on gas chromatography data has been published by Goedert and Guiochon (1).

The following eight thermal performance variables are of importance to the capillary chromatographer and should be considered in a good oven design (2):

- *Accuracy.* How close the actual oven temperature is to the temperature set point.

- *The range of operating temperatures.* Recent applications in capillary chromatography are expanding the high and low end of the operating temperature range. The oven should be able to maintain accurate temperatures close to ambient without cryogenic cooling. It should also reach upper temperatures in excess of 450°C.

- *The oven "heat-up" rate.* The ability of the oven to be heated precisely is important, especially at maximum temperature programming rates. Common phenomena, that occur during temperature programming, are a slight lag at the beginning of the ramp and an overshoot at final temperature. The temperature control system should be capable of minimizing these phenomena. A typical oven heat-up curve is given in Figure 4-1. The "worst-case" maximum programming rate of the oven is given by the slope of the curve at the maximum temperature. The maximum heat-up rate is sensitive to the system thermal mass; heater power level; the thermal "tightness" of the system (no thermal leaks); the heat transfer from heated zones (such as injection ports and detectors); and the nature of the columns, accessories, and other apparatus installed within the oven.

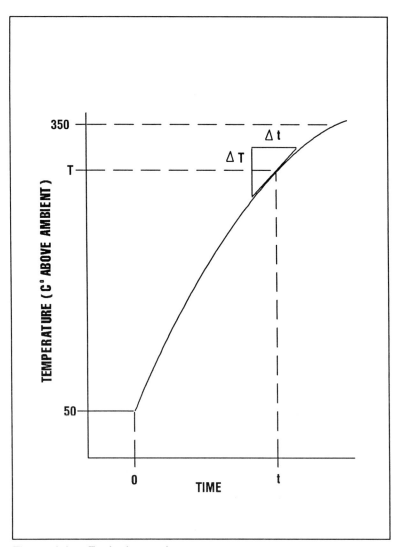

Figure 4-1.   Typical oven heat-up curve.

- *The oven cool-down rate* is the required time for the oven to cool from an elevated temperature to the initial set point temperature and become stable. Productivity is affected by the cool-down rate. The faster the oven can cool after a programmed run, the higher the sample throughput will be.

  Reliability in retention time is also dependent on the time required for the oven to reach equilibrium. Figure 4-2 illustrates the potential error in retention time as a function of the elapsed time after the instrument signals "READY."

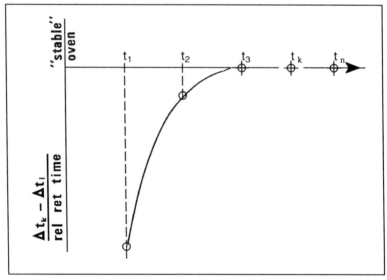

Figure 4-2.   Error in retention time as a function of elapsed time after the oven has reached a "READY" status.

- *Isothermal gradients* are the measure of the differences between the maximum and minimum temperatures observed within a restricted volume of the oven when thermally equilibrated at an isothermal temperature. The degree of the gradients is accepted as an indication of the quality of the chromatography oven.

- *Transient gradients* are temperature gradients that occur when the oven is in a thermally unstable condition, such as during heat-up or cool-down. These gradients are of greater magnitude than isothermal gradients and, if not reproducible, may prove critical to temperature programming in capillary gas chromatography.

- *Thermal noise* is defined as the periodic fluctuations in temperature around a stable average temperature. Retention time errors can be observed as a function of the amplitude and frequency of the thermal noise.

- *Ambient rejection* is defined as the ratio of the ambient temperature change to the oven temperature change. It describes the influence of ambient temperature changes on the temperature control electronics. The effect of changes in ambient temperature on the GC oven temperature is described by Rowland (3). For run-to-run retention time reproducibility, the ambient rejection should be as high as possible.

For high-performance chromatography, a high degree of oven thermal stability is required to achieve reproducible component resolution and retention for complex samples (4,5). Table 4-1 compares reproducibility in retention time for the analysis of a fatty acid methyl ester standard mixture. The capillary GC

Table 4-1. Retention Time Reproducibility for Selected Components in a Fatty Acid Methyl Ester Standard Mixture Analyzed on Different Commercial Gas Chromatographs.

Component	GC #1		GC #2		GC #3	
	RT	% Rel SD	RT	% Rel SD	RT	% Rel SD
$C_9H_{18}O_2$	1.563	0.30	1.600	3.38	2.033	0.64
$C_{10}H_{18}O_2$ (2-OH)	4.478	0.09	4.400	1.11	4.244	0.35
$C_{15}H_{30}O_2$	8.928	0.02	8.72	0.42	8.720	0.15
$C_{19}H_{38}O_2$	14.102	0.04	15.12	0.14	15.620	0.09

analysis was performed using three different commercial gas chromatography ovens. Since this sample is used as a calibration for microbial identification by pattern recognition, variations in retention time and the reproducibility in retention time observed for GC #2 and GC #3 would be considered unacceptable.

The desired degree of thermal stability in a GC oven is a factor of the engineering design. Performance expectations, such as retention time reproducibility translated into design specifications for oven stability, are necessary to ensure quality in high resolution gas chromatography data. Considerations in optimizing performance in an affordable commercial instrument are discussed in publications by Bente et al. (6,7).

II. DETECTORS

M. Wilson

High resolution open tubular columns can be used successfully with any of the commonly available gas chromatography detectors. An introduction to the various detectors and theory of operation are given in the recent text "Detectors for Gas Chromatography—A Practical Primer." (See Additional Reading at the end of this chapter.) In addition to the detectors listed in Table 4-2, the use of capillary columns with mass spectrometric and FT (Fourier transform) infrared detection is described in Chapter 5. To maintain the advantages of resolution and inertness in a capillary system, the column/detector interface should be understood and optimized. Optimal carrier gas type, and optimal flow rate for the gas chromatography detector may differ from those typically best suited for use with capillary columns. When connecting the capillary column and the detector, it is important to consider the following:

- Makeup gas type and flow rate
- Column end-positioning
- Dead volumes and active sites

Table 4-2.   Operating Conditions for Detectors Commonly Used
in Capillary Gas Chromatography.

| Type | Typical Samples | Sensitivity Range | Flow Rate (ml/min) | | |
			Carrier + Makeup	H_2	Air
FID	Hydrocarbons	10–100 pg 10 ppb–99%	20–60	30–40	200–500
TCD	General	5–100 ng 10 ppm–100%	15–30	n.a.	n.a.
ECD	Organo-halogens Chlorinated solvents & pesticides	0.05–1 pg 50 ppt–1 ppm	30–60	n.a.	n.a.
NPD	Organo-nitrogen & organo-phosphorus compounds	0.1–10 pg 100 ppt–0.1%	20–40	1–5	70–100
FPD (393 nm)	Sulfur compounds	10–100 pg 10 ppb–100 ppm	20–40	50–70	60–80
FPD (526 nm)	Phosphorus Compounds	1–10 pg 1ppb–0.1%	20–40	120–170	100–150

Each detector type has a different set of requirements for optimal use and is covered individually after a few general comments. There are essentially two ways of interfacing capillary columns. The column can be connected directly to the detector or via a secondary fitting installed in the detector base, as shown in Figure 4-3. Both of these configurations, if properly implemented, yield excellent chromatographic results. A convenient feature of using a secondary fitting is that the fitting can be moved easily from one detector to another. This provides a high degree of flexibility in detector selection while requiring only one makeup gas supply control. With direct connection, the makeup gas is usually hard-plumbed into the detector base or mixed with a support gas (such as hydrogen in a flame ionization detector), and each detector has its own makeup gas pneumatic control.

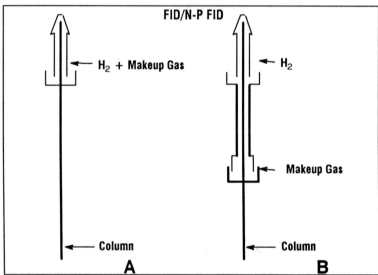

Figure 4-3.   Detector interfacing using two different techniques for adding makeup gas at the outlet of the column: A. Direct connection; B. Connection via a secondary fitting. Note that in both cases, the column extends to the tip of the flame jet. The makeup gas is added upstream of the column exit to sweep dead volume in the interface region.

Fused-silica capillary columns are remarkably flexible, and yet inherently straight (8). In comparison to glass capillary columns, fused silica columns can be connected to detectors without requiring end straightening. This allows placement of the column end as close to the detection zone as possible. Figure 4-4 illustrates the advantage of installing the column so that the end extends to within a few millimeters of the FID flame. This ensures that the system is truly all glass and eliminates the possibility of a contaminated area affecting the quality of the chromatographic system.

The combined use of makeup and carrier gas permits the detector sensitivity to be optimized with the column resolution. Table 4-2 gives the makeup gas and typical flow rate ranges for the different gas chromatography detectors. The makeup gas conveniently doubles as a sweep gas for the column exit and detector base.

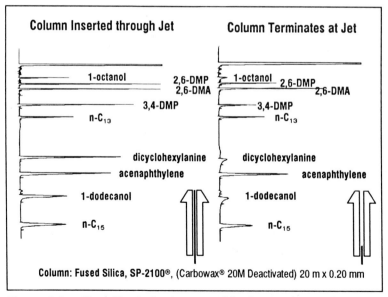

Figure 4-4.   The effect of column positioning on the quality of the chromatographic data.

Optimum settings for the column end position and for the makeup gas flows will ensure that active sites and dead volume in the detector interface are avoided.

Detector Types—Capillary Considerations

Flame Ionization Detector

When using a flame ionization detector (FID), the selection of the appropriate makeup gas is important to achieve the highest detector sensitivity. As shown in Figure 4-5, nitrogen is obviously a better choice for an FID than is helium. With helium, a 22% loss in FID sensitivity can be expected when compared to nitrogen; however, sensitivity is dependent not only on the type of makeup gas chosen but also on the flow rate of the makeup gas (Figure 4-6). The use of helium as a capillary makeup gas, in comparison to no makeup gas, is shown in Figure 4-7.

As indicated, column positioning is essential for optimal capillary chromatographic performance. With the flame ionization detectors currently designed for use with capillary columns, the column end is positioned 1 to 2 mm below the FID flame base as illustrated in Figure 4-8. If the end of a fused silica column protrudes into the flame, the polyimide coating will decompose, resulting in high signal offset and excess noise. Positioning too low will result in activity and dead volume at the column exit, as shown in Figure 4-4.

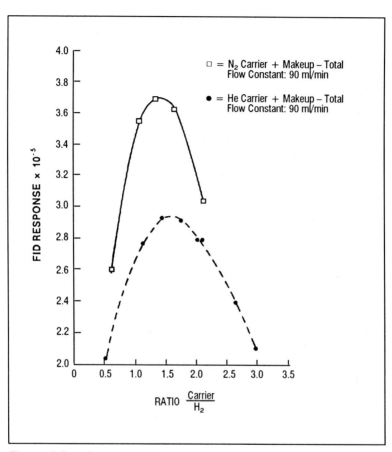

Figure 4-5.   Gas ratio-FID response curves.

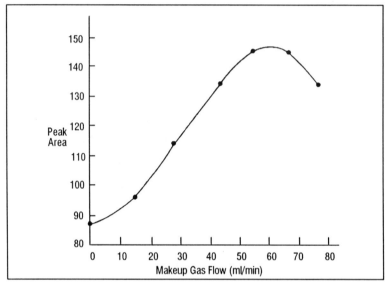

Figure 4-6.   A typical plot for an FID showing how the sensitivity (peak area) is dependent on the makeup gas flow rate. This curve is for a fixed hydrogen flow rate of 40 ml/min. For this detector, the maximum sensitivity occurs when the hydrogen/makeup gas flow ratio is around 0.67. Note: For H_2 = 30 ml/min, max is a 30-ml/min flow of makeup gas.

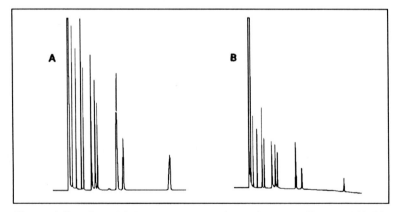

Figure 4-7.   Sensitivity versus total carrier gas flow.   (A) He makeup at 48 ml/min and (B) no makeup gas.

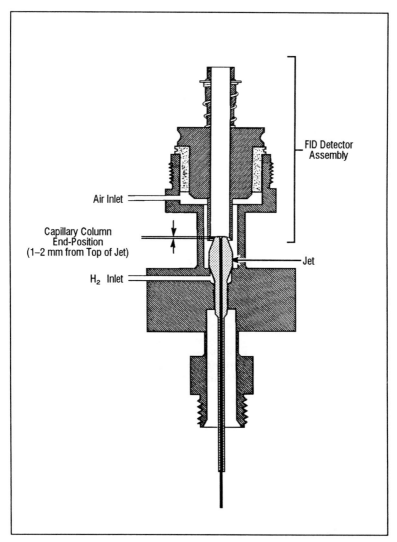

Figure 4-8. Flame ionization detector designed for use with capillary columns.

Thermal Conductivity Detector

Cell volume and carrier gas flow rate are critical to the sensitivity of the thermal conductivity detector (TCD) because it is a concentration detector. A pulse-modulated, single-filament TCD detector design (9) has dramatically improved the performance attainable with the TCD and capillary columns. Figure 4-9 shows the TCD design feature which permits the positioning of the end of a fused silica capillary column within 2 mm of the filament cell. Although the single filament design has an effective cell volume of only 3.5 µl, the use of makeup gas is recommended. Excellent results are achieved when the sum of the column flow and the makeup gas flow are maintained at a minimum of 5 ml/min. This ensures a rapid gas velocity sweeping the outside of the column and eliminates any band broadening in the detector/interface region.

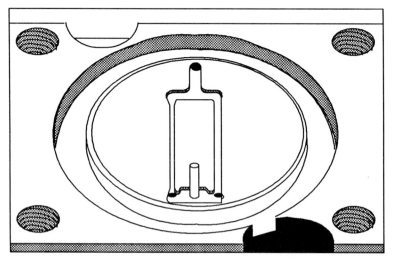

Figure 4-9.   Micro-TCD detector base with a 0.53 mm id fused silica column installed.

Helium is the recommended carrier and makeup gas for the TCD (thermal conductivity detector). The use of hydrogen can reduce the filament's oxide coating, resulting in changing response factors. An examination of the efficiency curves of a gas chromatography system, using an FID compared to that for the micro-TCD (Figure 4-10) shows that performance comparable to that of FID can be achieved using a TCD. The chromatograms illustrated in Figures 4-11 and 4-12 clearly show the inertness and dynamic range of the pulse-modulated, single-filament thermal conductivity detector design.

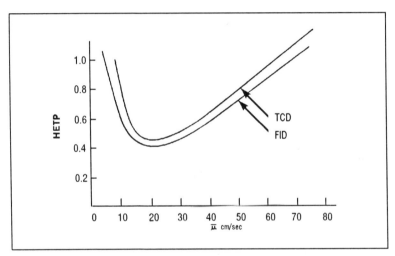

Figure 4-10. van Deemter curves using a 12 m x 0.2 mm fused silica column and either a TCD or an FID. Sample: 1 μl 1% n-dodecane in hexane (k = 6.8) split ratio 140:1. TCD flows: makeup gas = 4 ml/min, modulating gas flow = 18 ml/min.

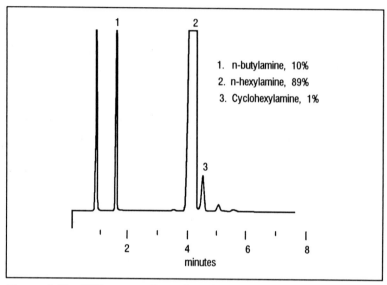

Figure 4-11. TCD separation of amines. 1 μl injected and split 20:1. Column: 10 m x 0.53 mm methyl silicone. Helium carrier at 21 cm/sec. Isothermal at 80°C.

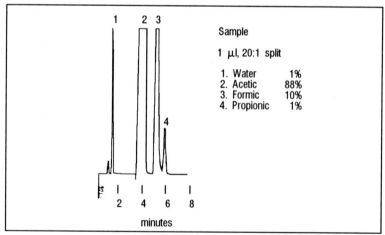

Figure 4-12. TCD separation of four volatile acids. 1 μl injected and split 20:1. Column: 10 m x 0.53 mm Carbowax 20M. Helium carrier at 22 cm/sec. Isothermal at 120°C.

Electron Capture Detector

To assure an equilibrium concentration of thermal electrons, an electron capture detector (ECD) requires the use of a moderating gas, such as nitrogen or argon/methane. This moderating gas can also be used as the sweep gas. Since the ECD is a concentration-dependent detector, sensitivity is inversely proportional to flow. It would appear that a low makeup gas flow would be preferred; however, the ECD cell volume should be large enough to accommodate a high surface area of beta-particle source and the flow should be high enough to sweep the cell volume effectively. Obviously, both optimum sensitivity and minimum band width cannot be obtained at the same flow rate. Depending on the requirements of the application, the makeup gas flow rate should be selected to achieve the desired results.

Generally, when using either helium or hydrogen as the carrier gas in a capillary column, a makeup gas flow rate of either nitrogen or argon/methane (5%) at 20–70 ml/min is satisfactory. Detector response as a function of moderating gas flow is shown in Figure 4-13. It is important to note the dynamic range of the ECD for trace halocarbon analysis and the stability in detector response over this concentration range. A schematic of the design of an ECD for use in high resolution gas chromatography is shown in Figure 4-14.

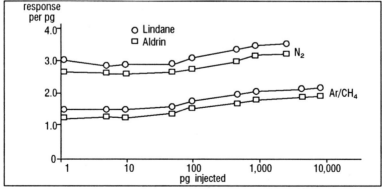

Figure 4-13. **ECD response as a function of the moderating gas used.**

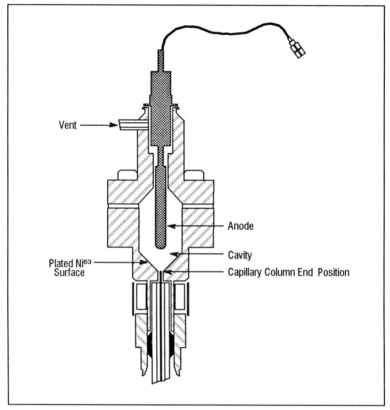

Figure 4-14. Diagram of an electron capture detector design showing the capillary column interface.

Nitrogen Phosphorus Detector

The best performance using a nitrogen phosphorus detector (NPD) is realized using helium as the makeup gas. The NPD hydrogen flow should be low (2–5 ml/min) with the helium makeup gas in the 20 to 30 ml/min range. Figure 4-15 illustrates the proper positioning of the column end at the tip of the jet. If the fused silica column extends beyond the jet, the polyimide coating can cause interference with the ionization mechanism in the detector. This results in noise, high offset, a wandering baseline, or a combination of all three.

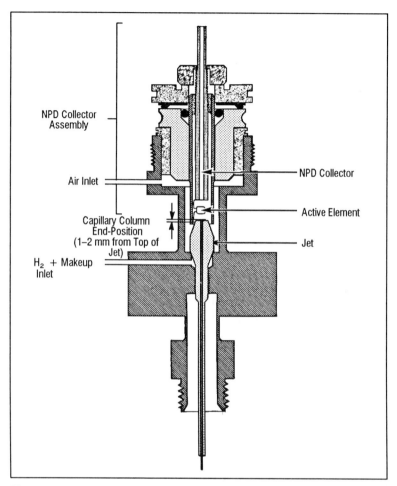

Figure 4-15. Diagram of a nitrogen-phosphorous detector designed for optimal performance with capillary columns.

Flame Photometric Detector

The positioning of the column end in a flame photometric detector (FPD) is especially critical, since most compounds containing sulfur or phosphorus are very active. To maintain the inertness of the fused silica capillary column, the effluent should exit the column at the flame base. This is accomplished in a recent FPD design, as shown in Figure 4-16. As with the FID and NPD, if a column extends into the flame, noise or offset problems result with the detector. Precise control of the gas flow to the detector virtually eliminates quenching of the detector response. Figure 4-17 illustrates the selectivity that results when the FPD is used with capillary columns for the analysis of sulfur compounds in petroleum naphtha. Interference from the concentrated hydrocarbon background is not observed.

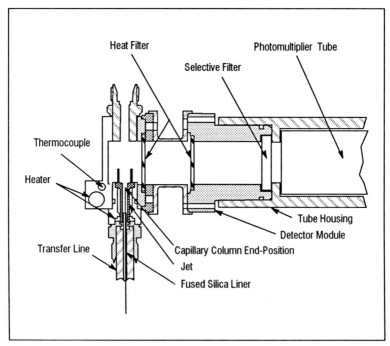

Figure 4-16. Design of a flame photometric detector optimized for use with capillary columns.

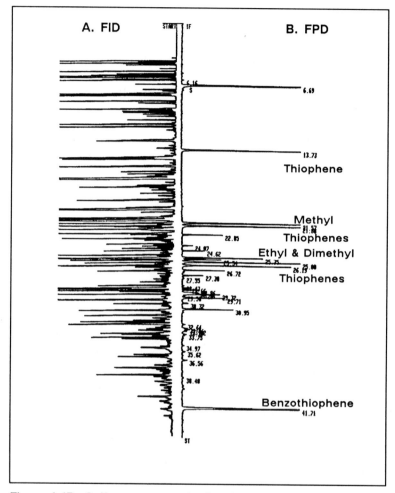

Figure 4-17. Sulfur compounds in the complex hydrocarbon mixture of petroleum naphtha. (Reproduced from Hewlett-Packard Application Brief, November 1986, Publication No. 43-5954-7615.)

Detector Sensitivity

Increased sensitivity is one of the major reasons for the surge of interest in high resolution gas chromatography. Improved sensitivity is realized with open tubular columns because of the following:

-   Capillary columns exhibit higher efficiencies than packed columns; thus the solute concentration per unit time is greater.
-   Capillary columns, especially fused-silica capillary columns, are much more inert than packed columns.
-   Detector sensitivity can be optimized through the use of a makeup gas.

The reasons for using the "right" makeup gas at the "right" flow rate can be summarized as follows:

1. Detector sensitivity is optimized by using the proper volumetric gas flows. There is an optimum carrier/makeup gas ratio that gives the greatest sensitivity.

2. Detector sensitivity is optimized by selecting the makeup gas which is most effective for the detector method used. For example, an FID gives the greatest response when nitrogen is used as the makeup gas.

3. The use of a makeup gas will permit the detector response to be optimized independent of both the carrier gas and the carrier gas flow rate. This is important because both the hydrogen carrier gas and nitrogen makeup gas are accommodated. This gives the best of both worlds—hydrogen carrier gas for the best chromatographic performance and nitrogen makeup gas for the greatest sensitivity.

Since the use of a makeup gas permits both the chromatography and the detector response to be optimized independently, the detector response is not sensitive to changes in the carrier gas flow rate. Consequently, the change in the carrier gas viscosity, as the column temperature is changed, has no effect on the detector sensitivity. This is not true for a detector that does not use a makeup gas. These detectors require that the carrier gas be flow controlled rather than pressure-regulated to prevent the detector response from changing as the column temperature changes.

III. DATA HANDLING

E. B. Smith

Introduction

In capillary GC systems, the major criterion for data acquisition is the ability of the device to measure the GC output with rapid sampling rates. The ability to easily collect and manipulate the data from complex separations is an additional consideration in capillary GC. For the chromatographer interested in high resolution analysis, recent advances in computer technology have provided the hardware for the development of a wide range of data handling devices for two-dimensional gas chromatography. The introduction and rapid evolution of computer technology into the chemical laboratory has shifted the performance provided by the mini- and super-mini-computers of a few years ago to the desk top and lab bench. Concurrently, the rapid technology and high competition levels in the computer-related electronics industries have increased the availability of microprocessor-based instrumentation.

These two occurrences have greatly increased the range of data handling alternatives for gas chromatography. When choosing an appropriate data-handling device, the chemist no longer has to sacrifice the minimum required feature set for an affordable instrument. The decision is now what additional features are needed in a data-handling product to help make data collection more effective. This section outlines the features available for the different types of data-handling products currently available.

Microprocessor-Based Integrators

The microprocessor-based integrator combines a strip chart recording mechanism, an analog-to-digital converter, and a microprocessor-based controller in a single cabinet. The integrator has keys to adjust paper speed, peak attenuation, and zero offset just like a strip chart recorder. The analog-to-digital converter converts the analog signal produced by the gas chromatographic detector to a digital signal for manipulation by software programs running on the integrator's microprocessor.

The microprocessor of the integrator allows it to determine the peak area and to perform a variety of calculations. Most standalone integrators perform area percent, height percent, internal standard, external standard, and normalization calculations. If the integrator is capable of doing a multilevel calibration, multiple standards are made up of concentrations bracketing the concentration range expected in the unknowns. The integrator's calibration routines fit a user-selected curve type to the multiple calibration points for each peak. The appropriate calibration curve fit is selected by the user, depending upon the type of GC detector being used. The use of multilevel calibration permits the integrator software to compensate for nonlinearities in the GC detector, thus yielding more accurate results in many cases.

The more sophisticated integrators can name and group peaks. The peak names are much more convenient and allow even the casual or nontechnical user to understand the results of the chromatographic analysis. The ability to group peaks allows one report to present information about specific components and aggregates of these components, providing more dimension to the data acquisition process.

"Top-of-the-line" standalone integrators provide BASIC programming of, instrument control of, and communication to a remote computer. With BASIC programming the user can customize the unit to the application. Special reporting, automated analysis with decision-making capability, and other utility functions can be accomplished through the use of BASIC programs. Many industry-specific applications have been developed for programmable integrators such as simulated distillation (10), gel permeation chromatography, retention index calculations, and PONA (paraffins, olefins, naphthenes, and aromatics) analysis (11).

Instrument control in the form of analog start-and-stop cabling is provided on all standalone integrators. The "top-of-the-line" instrument of most integrator manufacturers provides some form of control through digital connection. Digital connection integrators usually have fewer connection lines and simpler device connections than other integrators. Usually the inclusion of digital instrument control in an integrator is accompanied by digital data collection and digital instrument set point manipulation. For instance, the HP 3396A Computing Integrator uses the Instrument Network or INET. Using INET-compatible devices, all instrument set points, remote start/stop, bottle/sample number, and data can be transmitted over low-cost, two-conductor cables. Additionally, INET allows the inclusion of disk storage devices and external printing devices on the network.

Another digital interface supported by just about all "top-of-the-line" integrators is the RS-232-C data communications device. The RS-232-C digital data communications device has standardized electrical characteristics compatible with proprietary digital networks. Although the communication protocols used over the RS-232-C connection are almost always specific to the manufacturer, they are usually documented, and any software interface difficulty can be overcome by appropriate programming at the remote computer. The RS-232-C connection is usually used to connect the integrator to a remote computer. In many units the RS-232-C interface can be used for file transfer between the integrator and the computer. The files transferred typically contain A-to-D data-slice information, copies of the printed report, and instrument set points. The capabilities of the various RS-232-C interfaces vary dramatically and are beyond the scope of this chapter. See references (12,13,15) for more information on RS-232-C interface capabilities on integrators. For more information on RS-232-C communications, many books covering all levels of familiarity with RS-232-C are available on the market for the personal computer user.

When to Use an Integrator

The standalone integrator is useful for simple analyses that require data acquisition and reporting functions. Entry level integrator products typically feature a significant subset of the calculation procedures and control functions provided in the full-featured integrators. This level of product is excellent for production environments looking for decision-making capability and also for applications that use a strip chart recorder.

The next environment where integrators can be effectively applied is customized automated analysis. Applications in this category include:

- custom post-run calculation and reporting,
- decision-based automation, and
- buffered A-to-D (analog to digital) with integral printer/plotter.

Integrators with BASIC programming capability are very useful for these types of applications. Through the onboard BASIC, custom reporting and results calculations are accomplished using BASIC language keywords that access all of the chromatographic information present in the unit. Control of INET devices is also available using BASIC keywords. Additionally, access is provided to peripheral devices such as disk drives and devices attached to the RS-232-C port (12, 13). Industry specific applications, such as natural gas analysis and simulated distillation by GC, are done using BASIC and a computing integrator (14).

A final area where integrators are useful is as a starting point for growth to PC or minicomputer-based solutions. Initially, the integrator can provide users with a flexible data-processing environment. As data processing needs increase, the integrator can be used as a front end to a more powerful PC or minicomputer. The computer can then enhance the capabilities of one or more integrators or utilize the integrator as a smart peripheral for PC-based chromatography software. The integrator can act as an A-to-D with a local printer/plotter for an HP 3350A Laboratory Automation System. A PC can be interfaced to the integrator to act as a disk server. Some models of the Spectra Physics integrator line can also be used as intelligent A-to-Ds for PC-based chromatography software (15).

Personal Computer-Based Integrators/Data Systems

The migration of the personal computer (PC) from the home computer market and the business market to the scientific laboratory has provided a ready means for analytical data-handling manufacturers to build low-cost/medium-to-high-performance chromatography systems. The open architecture of most personal computers allows configuration of the systems to perform data acquisition and reduction, instrument control, and chromatogram display. The increased memory capability, increased processing speed, flexible user interface, and general popularity of the PC makes it useful for performing analyses that are not well suited to even the most sophisticated standalone integrators. The performance of a PC-based integrator is dependent on two factors: 1) the configuration of the hardware and 2) the design of the chromatographic software.

Hardware Configuration

Almost all of the PC-based chromatography data-handling systems use some type of buffered A-to-D interface. The interface can be:

- an A-to-D card that plugs into the PC chassis using one of the expansion slots,
- a standalone box that plugs into an accessory interface card via a cable (RS-232-C or IEEE-488), or
- a standalone integrator attached via an interface card and cable.

The buffering in the A-to-D interface off-loads the chore of collecting area slice information in real time from the A-to-D. This frees the PC workstation for handling multiple instrument signals and doing other types of processing while the GCs perform analyses. The modular structure of these PC systems allows the user to start with a small system and increase the hardware capacity over a period of time, thus reducing the size of the initial investment. Additionally, if new modules are added to the product line at a later date, system upgrade is facilitated.

In addition to the A-to-D interface, some PC-based systems require extra interface boards for interface to other analytical instrumentation. Peripherals, such as automated samplers, valve relay controllers, pump controllers (for LC), and generic digital data devices (bar code readers, balances, etc.) can also be interfaced to most PC-based systems. Some examples of extra interface boards include HP-IB Hewlett-Packard Interface Bus, IEEE-488 Interface Bus, and RS-232-C Serial Interface.

Finally, there are the standard hardware items normally associated with PC hardware configuration. These can include extra memory boards to increase the available internal memory for a program and various types and capacities of disk storage devices. Most chromatography software utilizes industry-standard memory and disk storage devices which are readily available for PCs.

Data-Handling Software

The other key component of the chromatographic data-handling system is the software. The software design will determine how effectively the underlying hardware potential can be utilized. Some chromatographic software is written so that it is intended to be the only application running on the PC at one time. This type of software effectively dedicates the PC to chromatographic data processing. In many situations, this dedicated configuration is not a problem. There may be significant processing involved; therefore, there would be little idle time on the PC for other applications. Additionally, many times the software is written to be very streamlined and to take advantage of certain hardware configurations. These system design decisions to dedicate a PC to chromatographic data processing can restrict the application of a PC but can increase chromatographic performance dramatically.

The other approach is to write PC software to integrate well with other commercially available hardware and software. This approach can yield software that performs effectively and a data-handling system that processes GC data more effectively. Chromatographic software can be developed by making additions or modifications to commercially available software. In addition, separate programs can be developed using commercially available software that can be designed into the chromatographic application. This provides the user with the ability to perform any desired data manipulation and relieves manufacturers of the burden of trying to include every potential function in their chromatography software.

PC-based data-handling software is usually a superset of that contained in standalone integrator products. The types of calculations performed, data storage capacity, data manipulation capabilities, etc. are usually enhanced versions of what is provided on standalone integrators.

When to Use a PC-Based Integrator/Data System

i. **Large quantities of data are to be collected and stored.**

The PC-based data system provides access to all of the resources of the PC. The greater resources of the PC include:

- large disk storage capacity (20–90 Mbytes),
- more refined operating system and user interface, and
- faster disk storage access times.

These resources are managed by a computer-operating system that is more sophisticated than those typically found in dedicated instrumentation. This increased sophistication provides a system with far more flexibility for the user and gives the user the ability to handle larger disk storage devices effectively. For example, MicroSoft Corporation's MicroSoft Disk-Operating System (MS-DOS)™ has commands to manipulate files on multiple disk devices. Each disk device contains a hierarchical file system that keeps the user group files together using a tree-structure directory.

ii. **Sophisticated data analysis is to be performed.**

Chromatographic data analysis can be done on sophisticated integrators or using off-the-shelf software. Many PC-based data analysis packages are available which permit the chromatographer to analyze results that were previously factored by hand or using a mini-computer. Spreadsheet packages are available which permit the further computation of chromatographic data.

iii. **CRT-based graphics are desirable.**

In some analyses, hard copy is not required for every run of the data. PC-based integrators are helpful in methods development environments where integration parameters are iteratively changed for a single data run, and high resolution graphics displays are desirable. Additionally, since the CRT display system is modular in design, the display can be replaced as more advanced models are introduced.

iv. **Chromatographic data is to be used in reports.**

In addition to data analysis software, there are many software packages available for PCs for doing word processing, bar charting, line charting, pie charting, and project management. These packages allow the PC hardware to be used for data acquisition, data reduction, and final report production. The common hardware base for all these packages allows data to be moved between the various phases efficiently.

Minicomputer-Based Data Systems

The minicomputer-based data system has been used in the analytical laboratory for several years now for chromatography data acquisition. Technically, the minicomputer preceded the introduction of the personal computer by some years. From a cost analysis perspective, the minicomputer still provides a cost-effective solution for high throughput, routine analysis laboratories that have many channels of data acquisition. The localized structure of the minicomputer can solve the following problems:

- centralized data storage in environments that require limited physical access to data,
- protection of computer equipment from harsh environments, and
- ease of system maintenance.

If other applications are run on the computer (laboratory information management, complex numerical analyses, multi-user access to data) minicomputer-based systems can still provide the necessary processing power and system resources to do multiple applications effectively.

When to Use a Minicomputer-Based Chromatography System

i. **Large quantities of data are to be collected and archived.**

Minicomputer operating systems are typically designed to handle multiple large disk storage devices that are concurrently accessed by multiple users. Additionally, these systems typically support high-speed tape drive systems to allow the disk devices to be backed up and to move data tape for archive purposes. A medium-sized data system may contain two disk drives (each capable of holding 571 million bytes) and an open-reel tape drive. A system with this storage capacity could support a LIMS (laboratory information management systems) and a chromatography acquisition system used by ten users' terminals and 10 to 15 A-to-Ds for instrument interface. Depending on the mix of operations performed by each user, there may still be system capacity to perform other tasks, such as communications with other computers.

ii. **Data is to be combined with LIMS.**

Laboratory information management systems (LIMS) are still primarily implemented on minicomputer systems. This is primarily due to the minicomputer operating system multitasking/multiuser nature. The LIMS system typically runs concurrently with data acquisition software on the same computer. Some programs running on the computer accept data from the A-to-D subsystem and store the raw data, or maybe even processed data, on the disk. Results from the processing can be input automatically into the LIMS system or manually input by another user with LIMS software. The minicomputer environment provides users with the ability to run the two applications simultaneously on one computer. Additionally, both applications can pass the data using the shared disk drives.

iii. Multiuser access is needed for a single pool of data.

In environments where many users require a single set of data, the minicomputer based system can do very well. Multiuser access to data is usually provided by most minicomputer operating systems, and this facility can be utilized by the chromatographic applications. Problems with redundant data sets being updated differently are eliminated; this improves data integrity. Also, for environments requiring data security, it is far easier to control access to one set of data than to many distributed copies of that data. A final advantage to multiuser access to a single pool of data is the reduced cost of data storage. This is especially important in environments that must keep large quantities of data available for long periods of time as required by regulation.

Conclusion

The current state of data-handling technology is such that the user need not sacrifice features and performance strictly based on price. Basic chromatographic data reduction and reporting can be performed on the standalone integrator, the PC-based chromatography workstation, and the minicomputer-based laboratory automation system. The differences among the systems are dependent upon the application of the data handling device. The standalone integrator is best utilized in applications that require low-cost, simple custom reporting and/or minimum data storage requirements. Increased data storage, more complex computation, and more sophisticated data manipulation requirements necessitate the use of the more powerful PC-based chromatography systems. Applications requiring large data storage capacities, multiuser access to common data and concurrent laboratory information, and management system access are currently implemented on minicomputer-based chromatography systems.

References

1. Goedert, M., and G. Guiochon. 1973. *Anal Chem* 45:1180–1187.

2. Welsh, P. August 1988. *HP Technical Paper No. GC-68.* Publication No. 43-5952-5769.

3. Rowland, F. 1982. *Amer Lab* 14:110–114.

4. Bente, B. May 1979. *HP Application Note No. 228-14.* Publication No. 43-5953-1441.

5. Green, L. E., and E. Matt. September 1982. *HP Technical Paper No. 100.* Publication No. 43-5953-1656.

6. Bente, H. B., W. I. Buffington, R. A. Brown, R. P. Rhodes, and T. M. Przybylski. 1984. *Amer Lab* 16:60–67.

7. Bente, B., P. Welsh, A. Kaufman, and R. Brown. 1984. *Amer Lab* 16:50–54.

8. Dandeneau, R., P. Bente, T. Rooney, and R. Hiskes. 1979. *Amer Lab* 11(9):61–69.

9. Messaros, D. W., C. E. Law, R. H. Kolloff, R. C. Gearhart, and R. R. Freeman. April 1984. *20th International Symposium, Advances in Chromatography.* New York.

10. Firor, R. L. January 1988. *HP Application Note No. 228-60.* Publication No. 43-5954-9198.

11. Huber, H. L., J. de Jong, Han Spaans, and D. Schipluiden. April 1982. *HP Application Note No. 228-24.* Publication No. 12-5953-0071.

12. Smith, E. B. January 1988. *HP Application Note No. 228-59.* Publication No. 43-5954-9195.

13. Smith, E. B. March 1988. *HP Application Note No. 228-61.* Publication No. 43-5954-9208.

14. Firor, R. L. January 1988. *HP Application Note No. 228-60.* Publication No. 43-5954-9198.

15. Rooney, T. 1986. *Spectra Physics Chromatography Review* 13(2):2–7.

Additional Reading

1. Buffington, R., and M. Wilson. 1987. *Detectors for Gas Chromatography—A Practical Primer.* Hewlett-Packard.

2. Borman, S. A. 1985. *Anal Chem* 57:1256A–1271A.

CHAPTER 5. MULTIDIMENSIONAL GAS CHROMATOGRAPHY AND HYPHENATED TECHNIQUES

I. MULTIDIMENSIONAL GC
W. Dale Snyder

Introduction

Multidimensional gas chromatography (MD-GC) uses two or more coupled columns to achieve separations not attainable with a single column. Advances in column and instrument technology have made MD-GC an easy-to-use technique for difficult separations. This chapter provides a general introduction to MD-GC. The reader is referred to the additional reading list at the end of the chapter for comprehensive coverage of the technique and its applications.

With the widespread use of capillary columns during the last decade, users have found their samples to be more complex than originally thought, and this has created a demand for greater resolution. It was soon discovered that the use of a long, high resolution capillary column was accompanied by long analysis times, high cost, insufficient capacity, and no guarantee of the required resolution. The solution—more selectivity and greater capacity. MD-GC optimizes the selectivity and capacity differences of different kinds of columns by combining them in such a way to achieve the maximum resolution of different concentrations of analytes in the shortest possible time.

A simple two-dimensional gas chromatography (2D-GC) system operates as follows. Sample is injected into a precolumn where the first separation occurs. The effluent normally enters a monitor detector, but a selected portion or several portions, called heartcuts, may be diverted to an analytical column. The cut(s) undergo a second separation on the column prior to entering the analytical detector. Switching of the precolumn effluent is achieved with mechanical valves or a pneumatic switch, such as that invented by D. R. Deans in 1968 and frequently called a Deans' switch (1). A cold trap, located at the inlet of the analytical column, may be used to collect cuts and reinject them as narrow plugs onto the analytical column. Additional features might include precolumn backflush, multiple detectors, etc., as needed for a given application.

Applications best suited for MD-GC depend on the type of sample, types of detectors, and whether trace levels (<ng) of components must be identified. Applicable sample types are those that are complex (foods, flavors, environmental, etc.) or those that require capacity or selectivity differences for separation (e.g., natural gas). Applicable detectors are those that employ library search for identification such as MSD (mass sensitive detector), IRD (infrared detector), etc. Pure, well-resolved components are required at these detectors for unambiguous identification. If trace components must be identified but are below detector threshold for good measurement, MD-GC can provide retention indices from precolumns and analytical columns.

Definition of Multidimensional Chromatography

There is some confusion in the literature about the definition of multidimensional gas chromatography (MD-GC). Hyphenated techniques such as GC-MS, GC-IR, etc., are often referred to as MD-GC even if only a single column separation is used. These systems involve multidimensional detection and should not be considered multidimensional chromatography. Such techniques are multidimensional in *information* generated about the sample but usually employ one-dimensional chromatography.

Bertsch (2) has reviewed MD-GC and offers the following definition:

"Two-dimensional GC should be based on either of the following principles:

– Two columns of different selectivity in combination with a system (integration, MS identification, etc.) which will permit assignment of retention indices.

   – Two columns of different selectivity and a device (prep scale collection tube, valve, etc.) to transfer a portion of a chromatographic run selectively from one into another column."

The following more general definition is proposed:

Multidimensional chromatography is a separation process in which a single sample is subjected to a sequence of chromatographic separations, each of which:

   – Acts upon all or part of the separated components from a previous chromatographic step and

   – Differs in its relative selectivity and/or capacity.

The emphasis is on *chromatographic* dimensionality. For example, two columns in one inlet leading to two detectors is not 2D-GC but simply two parallel one-dimensional separations. The above definition includes all types of chromatographic separations—HPLC (high pressure liquid chromatography), GPC (gel permeation chromatography), SFC (supercritical fluid chromatography), TLC (thin layer chromatography), etc. It also includes multiple separations where only the capacity is changed.

The important distinction in any multidimensional technique is between separation and detection. Chromatography is a separation technique that is completely independent of detection method. Some consider the term "hyphenated technique" to mean multiple detection (MS-MS, IR-MS, etc.), while others include the separation technique (GC-MS, LC-IR, etc.). Further confusion arises in describing coupled chromatographic techniques (LC-GC, TLC-GC, etc.). These are not only considered to be hyphenated techniques, but are also referred to as orthogonal techniques. In any discussion it is imperative that the meaning of "multidimensional" be clear. For example, GC-GC-IR-MS implies 2D-GC with IR-MS detection. This may be the best approach for a clear understanding of a multidimensional method.

Operation and Utility of MD-GC: A Simple Two-Dimensional System

The simplest MD-GC system is the 2D-GC (two-dimensional GC system) illustrated in Figure 5-1. Sample is injected into the precolumn (packed or capillary) where the first dimension of separation occurs. Selected portions are heartcut to the analytical column, usually a capillary, where the second separation occurs. The columns may be in the same or different ovens. Cutting is achieved either with a mechanical valve as shown, or with a pneumatic or Deans' switch. The simplicity of a home-made Deans' switched system in a HP 5880A, and some of the applications potential of 2D-GC, was demonstrated by Phillips *et al.* in 1982 (3). Additional features may be present such as precolumn backflush, as shown for a pneumatically switched system in Figure 5-2.

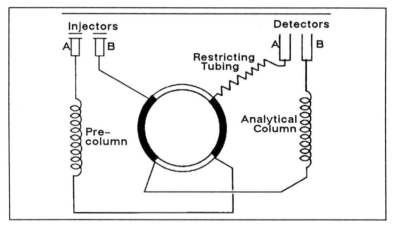

Figure 5-1.   Schematic of gas flow paths with the Valco four-port rotary valve. In one valve position the flow paths are (1) injector A to precolumn to valve to restrictor tubing to detector A, and (2) injector B to valve to analytical column to detector B. In the other valve position, the flows are (1) injector A to precolumn to valve to analytical column to detector B, and (2) injector B to valve to restrictor tubing to detector A. (Reproduced with permission from B. M. Gordon, C. E. Rix, and M. F. Borgerding, *J. Chromatogr. Sci.*, *23* (1985) 1-10).

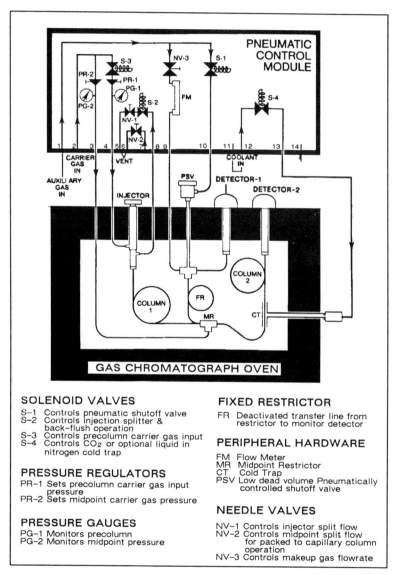

SOLENOID VALVES

S–1 Controls pneumatic shutoff valve
S–2 Controls injection splitter &
     back-flush operation
S–3 Controls precolumn carrier gas input
S–4 Controls CO_2 or optional liquid in
     nitrogen cold trap

PRESSURE REGULATORS

PR–1 Sets precolumn carrier gas input
     pressure
PR–2 Sets midpoint carrier gas pressure

PRESSURE GAUGES

PG–1 Monitors precolumn
PG–2 Monitors midpoint pressure

FIXED RESTRICTOR

FR Deactivated transfer line from
    restrictor to monitor detector

PERIPHERAL HARDWARE

FM Flow Meter
MR Midpoint Restrictor
CT Cold Trap
PSV Low dead volume Pneumatically
    controlled shutoff valve

NEEDLE VALVES

NV–1 Controls injector split flow
NV–2 Controls midpoint split flow
     for packed to capillary column
     operation
NV–3 Controls makeup gas flowrate

Figure 5-2.   Schematic diagram of SGE pneumatic column switching (PCS) system. (Reproduced with permission from Scientific Glass Engineering PTY. LTD.)

The utility of this simple system becomes apparent when we consider the different ways a precolumn may be used. The precolumn may be:

i.   A high resolution column (>100,000 plates) for separation of a complex mixture into narrow cuts for further separation on an analytical column.

ii. A high-capacity column (>1 microgram) to separate solvent, major components, or derivatizing reagents from trace or other components of interest and to protect the analytical column and detector from overload or damaging reagents.

iii. A sample prep column to get rid of unwanted material and cut only the components of interest to the analytical column.

iv. A chemical trap to retain specific compound families of no interest, or a reactor to derivatize families prior to analysis on the analytical column.

v.   A concentrator column for collecting sample in dilute solution from multiple injections (4), or large volume single injections (5).

vi. An uncoated column with on-column injector to operate as a programmed temperature vaporizer.

When is MD-GC Necessary?

MD-GC is certainly an excellent candidate for methods development. It can minimize the time and effort required to determine if a single column will do the job, and which one to use. The partial list of precolumn uses in the previous section shows some applications for the technique. There are more general guidelines that can be used to determine if MD-GC is the method of choice.

The need for MD-GC in a given application is determined by the type of sample, method of detection, and relative concentration of analytes. The sample types that require MD-GC are:

- Complex samples (petroleum products, foods and flavors, environmental, etc.), or

- Samples that cannot be completely separated by a single mechanism (natural gas, refinery gas, etc.).

What do we really mean by a "complex" sample? Schomburg, et al. (6) have described complex mixtures as those that "may contain components

- with a wide range of concentrations,

- with a wide range of polarities,

- with a wide range of volatilities,

- with different thermal/catalytic stabilities,

- that appear in a chromatogram with numerous over-lappings, and

- that belong to the same group of isomers.

No simple chromatographic procedure can deal with all of these."

Any detector that uses library search (MSD,IRD) or elemental analysis (atomic emission) benefits from MD-GC. For reliable identification, single, pure, well-resolved peaks are required at the detector. Chemometrics can be used to deconvolute unresolved peaks with sophisticated algorithms, but there are limitations to this approach.

In many cases, trace (<ng) components must be identified, yet the sample amount is too small for reliable MS or IR spectra. MD-GC can be used to obtain retention indices on precolumns and analytical columns of different polarity. This is frequently sufficient for positive identification. Practically every application

area where GC is used has some samples that can benefit from MD-GC.

Recent Advances

MD-GC is certainly not a new technique. A system was described in 1962 by Mikkelsen and Spencer(7) for the analysis of trace impurities in vinyl chloride. The need today is to separate very complex mixtures at trace levels. Advances in chromatographic hardware and column technology during the last 10–15 years have improved the ability to handle such mixtures.

Some advances that make MD-GC a viable technique include the following:

i. Fused silica capillary columns which provide not only high resolution and inertness, but also ease of manipulation. Most MD-GC work in the 1970s used glass capillaries. MD-GC with rigid, fragile glass capillaries was sufficiently tedious to confine its use to the research laboratory.

ii. 530 μm fused silica capillary columns which provide the capacity of packed columns with the inertness, ruggedness, and ease of handling of fused silica capillaries. Packed glass columns suffer from the same shortcomings as glass capillaries, and in addition, are too active for trace analysis.

iii. PLOT and micropacked capillary columns which fill a niche not covered by WCOT capillaries by providing high resolution fixed gas analysis and unique separation of isomers.

iv. Microvolume valves/pneumatic switches. Low dead volume column-switching hardware, designed specifically for use with fused silica capillaries has recently become commercially available.

Some Illustrative Chromatograms

Figure 5-3 is a chromatogram of a petroleum sample on a polar precolumn. The same sample using the polar precolumn in series with a nonpolar analytical column is shown in Figure 5-4. Selected heartcuts from seven different runs are illustrated in Figure 5-5.

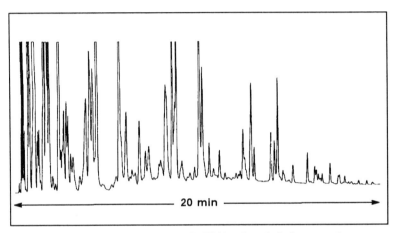

—————— 20 min ——————

Figure 5-3. Chromatogram of PNA (naphtha) sample on a precolumn using an HP 5880A Gas Chromatograph and an SGE pneumatic column switching system. Precolumn: 12 m x 0.2 mm x 0.33 μm film of 50% phenyl-methyl silicone. Carrier: helium, 30 cm/sec. Injector temperature: 250°C. Detector (FID) temperature: 325°C. Sample introduction: 0. 2 μl, 200:1 automated split injection with HP 7673A Automated Liquid Sampler. Oven profile: 35° C for 5 min programmed at 5 °C/min to 130°C for 10 min.

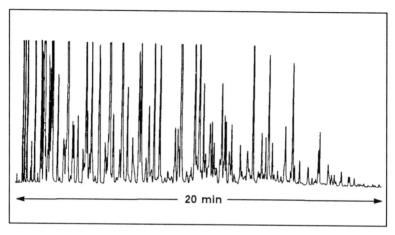

Figure 5-4.　Chromatogram of　PNA (naphtha) sample on the precolumn　and　analytical　column　in　series. Analytical column: 12 m x 0.2 mm x 0.33 μ m film methyl silicone. Legend same as Figure 5-3.

Examination of these figures shows that the peak overlap that occurred on the precolumn may be resolved on the analytical column, but new overlap may occur on the analytical column. Therefore, heartcutting has distinct advantages over simply using two different columns in series.　Note　also that the narrower the cut from the precolumn, the greater the chance for complete resolution on the analytical column (cf. cuts 1 and 7 vs. 4 and 5).

Some shortcomings of the simple two-dimensional system (2D-GC) are apparent.　To achieve maximum resolution of a complex sample requires many narrow cuts selected so that components from one cut do not overlap those from another. For example, cuts 1, 3, 5, and 7 could be analyzed in a single run with no overlap.　Multiple runs are required to resolve complex samples effectively.　There is no *a priori* way to decide when and how wide to make cuts.　With very complex samples the best solution probably would be an added dimension of prefractionation (with a technique such as HPLC,

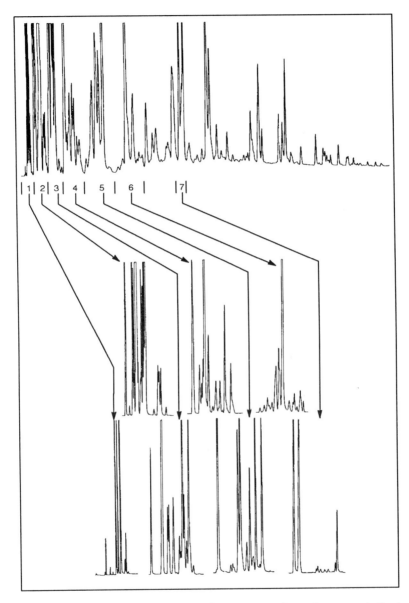

Figure 5-5. Selected heartcuts from a precolumn to an analytical column without intermediate cold trapping. Legend same as Figures 5-3 and 5-4.

SFC, GPC, etc.) for 2D-GC. The worst-case analysis is a complex sample, limited amount, and no 2D-GC established method. Nondestructive detectors followed by total effluent trapping for reanalysis may be required (8). Data handling and display is another area that needs improvement. Creative graphics software for relating precolumn cuts with analytical chromatograms is desirable, since complexity increases with the number of cuts.

Conclusions

MD-GC is an easy-to-use technique for deriving maximum advantage from the separating power available from modern columns and instrumentation. In many cases, MD-GC can reduce the sample preparation work load, as well as increase speed and reliability for the analysis of complex samples. Chapter 8 gives some practical applications which demonstrate the use of capillary columns in multidimensional separations.

II. HYPHENATED TECHNIQUES

Capillary GC-MS

P. Goodley

For over 30 years, mass spectrometers have been used as gas chromatographic (GC) detectors. During this time, the capability and reliability of the mass spectrometer (MS), and the reproducibility of analytical data, has increased inversely with the cost of commercial MS systems. A modern combined GC-MS system is capable of performing an analysis on a complex matrix of 25 compounds within 30 minutes. Both the quantitative and qualitative information is provided to the analyst in a short period of time. The GC-MS data system is used to process each GC peak found during the analysis and to compare the mass spectrum from each GC peak to a mass spectrum from a library of standards stored in a resident data base (9,10). A computer pattern-matching routine is used to compare the known standard spectrum to that of the unknown. A correlation coefficient for the known to the unknown spectrum is supplied to the analyst as additional structural information. By combining the separation capability of GC, with the specific mass spectral patterns obtained from the MS, and the quantifiable information obtained from the peak areas, the power and cost-effectiveness of GC-MS becomes evident.

The popularity of the mass spectrometer as a detector for gas chromatography has been due primarily to the amount of specific information that may be gathered from GC-MS. When the mass spectrometer is used as a GC detector, it responds differentially and more universally than other detectors. Instead of responding to specific classes of compounds, as an electron capture detector would respond only to halogens or as a flame ionization detector would respond to hydrocarbons, the mass spectrometer responds to all types of organic compounds (10–12). The mass spectrometer, unlike other GC detectors, responds to mass, a physical property common to all organic compounds.

The spectrum consists of a unique bar graph in which the height of the bars represents the relative abundance of the most abundant ions of each individual compound as a function of the mass (13,14). These ions give information concerning the molecular weight and the most electronically stable ion fragments from the original molecule. These unique fragments may be matched or interpreted to characterize a molecule based on its atomic structure. Figure 5-6 shows a typical electron impact (EI) mass spectrum of acetone. Note the ion fragments at the mass-to-charge ratios (m/z) 15 and 43. These ion fragments represent the parts of the molecule that broke off from the parent molecule. Also, note the parent molecule of acetone at m/z 58, a valuable piece of information to the analyst. The spectra produced by all electron impact ion sources for MS systems have been found to be reproducible and unique for most organic compounds (14–16).

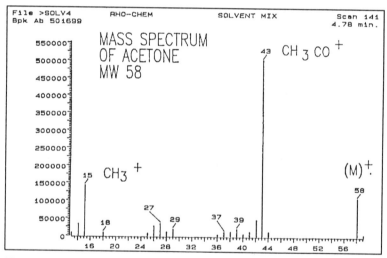

Figure 5-6.   Electron-impact mass spectrum of acetone showing the molecular ion at m/z 58, the base peak at m/z 43, and the methyl fragmentation at m/z 15.

In addition to qualitative information, the mass spectrometer also provides quantitative information for each component. The quantitative information is obtained two ways:

1) By using the sum of all ion current signals to generate a plot of ion current versus time, or

2) To extract any individual ion currents for any mass fragments chosen by the analyst to form additional plots.

These two ion-current profiles are known, respectively, as the total ion current (TIC) and extracted ion profile (EIP). Both signals may be treated electronically as GC signals, having associated retention times, response factors, and integrated areas. Figure 5-7 shows the TIC of an underivatized drug standard mixture. The TIC is followed by six extracted ion profiles (EIP) that are the characteristic ions from each compound in the mixture. As with the GC, the separated individual GC peaks may be quantified with precision and reproducibility.

Another powerful capability of MS is that of quantifying coeluting or nonseparated GC peaks by using the EIP process to extract components having a mass of interest, and treating each extracted mass as a separate GC trace. The technique is used often to reduce GC method development time and to scout for target compounds in complex matrices. It is also used as a standard method in drug metabolism. Isotopically labeled molecules coelute with the drug of interest. The EIP process is then used to extract components within the mass of interest and the findings used as internal standards for the specified biosystem (10).

Components of a Mass Spectrometer

A mass spectrometer consists of four main parts: 1) the ion source, 2) the mass analyzer, 3) the detector, and 4) the instrument control and data-handling system. A block diagram of the parts of a mass spectrometer (MS) with a data system is shown in Figure 5-8. Figure 5-9 depicts a typical quadrupole mass spectrometer consisting of an electron impact ion

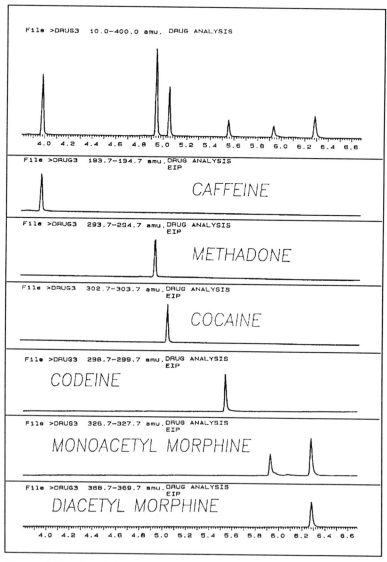

Figure 5-7. Total ion chromatogram (TIC) of a drug standard mixture of caffeine, methadone, cocaine, codeine, monoacetyl morphine and heroin, and the six extracted ion profiles (EIP) of the molecular ion for each compound.

source, a quadrupole mass analyzer, a continuous-dyanode electron multiplier, along with an instrument controller/ data-handling system. The system is similar to that of the Hewlett-Packard 5970 and 5971 Mass Selective Detectors (MSD).

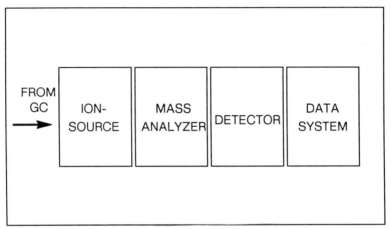

Figure 5-8. Block diagram of the components of a typical mass spectrometer.

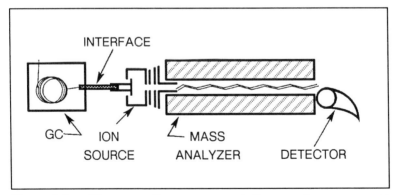

Figure 5-9. Diagrammatic representation of a mass spectrometer with an electron-impact (EI) ion source, a quadrupole mass analyzer, and a continuous-dyanode electron multiplier. The GC interface is capillary direct as commonly used in the HP 5970 and 5971 MSD.

The Ion Source

The two most accepted ways to create ions in mass spectrometers are by electron impact ionization (EI) and chemical
ionization (CI). Thus far, the largest amount of mass spectra
have been obtained by electron impact ionization. A
diagrammatic representation of an EI source is shown in
Figure 5-10. Currently, mass spectral library data bases exist
that contain upward of 120,000 EI mass spectra. The largest
collection of mass spectra is the EPA/NIH data collection which
is used to compare and to match spectra when analyzing for
target compounds in drug and environmental work (15).

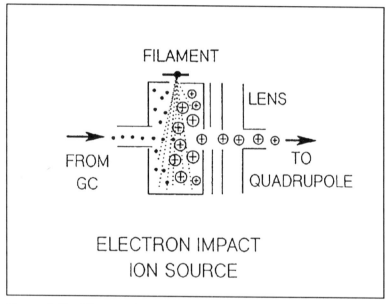

Figure 5-10. Electron-impact ion source used for generating ions
from vaporized molecules eluting from a gas
chromatographic column.

The Mass Analyzer

Five basic types of mass analyzers have been used to separate the ions once formed in the ion source. The five types of mass analyzers are 1) magnetic, 2) electrostatic, 3) time-of-flight, 4) ion cyclotron resonance, and 5) quadrupole and variations on the quadrupole (10–16). The ion trap is a variation of the quadrupole analyzer utilizing an ion-trapping process. The magnetic and the quadrupole analyzers are the most widely accepted and are used to generate the majority of mass spectra in the library data bases. The mass separation in the quadrupole mass analyzer occurs due to the ion response in the RF/DC field (10,12). A mass spectrum is obtained by sweeping the field and recording the ion currents obtained as each ion strikes the detector.

The Detector

Many different types of detectors have been used in mass spectrometers, but the most popular are the discrete dyanode electron multiplier and the continuous dyanode electron multiplier. Both of these devices have high gain amplification characteristics in the range of 10^7. The high gain capabilities of the electron multiplier are what allow the detection of very low femtoampere ion currents. The low current detector capability is responsible for the extreme sensitivity of mass spectrometers when used as detectors for a gas chromatograph. Most quadrupole MS systems are capable of detecting low picogram quantities of volatile compounds with a signal-to-noise ratio of greater than 10:1.

GC-MS Interfaces

Interfacing a GC to a mass spectrometer prior to the advent of fused silica capillary columns was an important consideration due to the differences in the pressure environments required by each instrument (11). A large number of interfacing devices were created to go from the high-pressure environment created by the packed GC column effluent to the low pressure (vacuum) required by the mass spectrometer. The interfaces were designed to minimize the losses of the analyte by either temperature gradients (cold spots) or poor molecular separation (yield). These interfacing devices became known as molecular separators due to their efficiency in removing the unwanted helium carrier gas, which was the major contributor to the high-pressure gas load of the mass spectrometer.

The three GC-MS packed column interfaces used most often are 1) silicone rubber membrane, 2) the effusive tube, and 3) the molecular jet separator (11,12). By far the most accepted molecular separator used for packed column GC-MS is the molecular jet separator. Figure 5-11 depicts a jet interface. This first jet separator interface was constructed by Rahage using stainless steel. Later, most jet separators were made of glass to minimize chemical reactivity and maximize throughput and sensitivity (11–13,15). The jet uses the principle of momentum to separate the molecules of helium from the heavier analyte molecules in the gas stream. The exiting jet is drawn down to a small orifice causing the GC effluent gas to be accelerated close to supersonic speed. The analyte, due to its greater momentum, traverses the gap between the two jets more efficiently than the lighter helium, which diverges from a straight line-of-sight and is pumped away. The jet separator

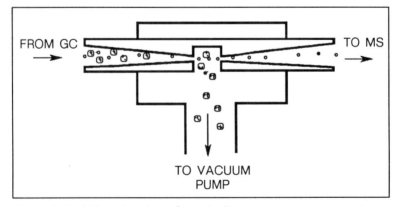

Figure 5-11. Diagram of a molecular jet separator.

is still used successfully when interfacing packed and large diameter (>0.5 mm id) FSWCOT columns to the mass spectrometer.

Capillary Mass Spectrometer Interfaces

The introduction of fused silica capillary columns (17) provided the much needed high resolution GC separation coupled with the low gas flow required by the mass spectrometer. The fused silica capillary columns offer two ways to interface the GC to the mass spectrometer: a direct coupling, or a splitting device known as the open split interface (OSI). The OSI (18–21) allows a fixed leak into the mass spectrometer without creating a vacuum inside the GC column or affecting the column resolution. The interface was designed when glass capillary columns frequently had an id greater than 0.35 mm. A vacuum on the column would have been created at the injector port by using a direct interface, and vacuum at the injection port creates a large air leak into the mass spectrometer, resulting in poor sensitivity for the MS. Therefore, open split interface is recommended for FSWCOT columns of internal diameter greater than 0.32 mm.

A diagram of the open split interface (21) and the gas flow scheme is shown in Figure 5-12. The auxiliary helium carrier gas provides a coaxial gas sleeve around the sample exit and acts as a hydraulic coupling. The purge gas also provides additional make-up gas to balance any change in column effluent flow due to the change in the helium viscosity as the column oven temperature is programmed.

Figure 5-13 shows a direct capillary coupling to the MS source. This type of interface is the simplest and optimal for small bore (<0.2 mm id) capillary columns (22). Columns having short-lengths and internal diameters larger than 0.35 mm present problems when used with mass spectrometers with a low-capacity, high-vacuum pumping system due to the difference in conductance (12) of the columns. The conductance of a small tube varies as a function of the diameter to the 3.5th power. A small change in the diameter causes a large change in the conductance or flow of the gas through the capillary. Thus, a large-capacity vacuum system is required for capillary columns larger than 0.2 mm id.

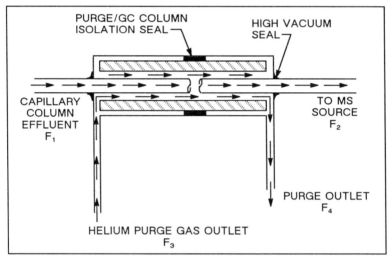

Figure 5-12. The open split capillary interface for coupling large bore capillary columns to mass spectrometers with limited capacity vacuum systems.

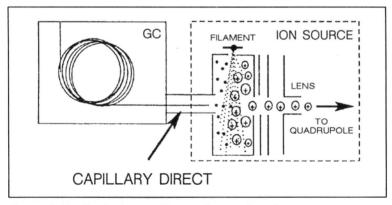

Figure 5-13. Typical capillary direct interface to a mass spectrometer with an electron-impact ion source.

Applications of GC-MS

Applications of GC-MS are almost unlimited for the analytical organic chemist. GC-MS is used with equal success in research and development and quality control. Figure 5-14 shows an example of the use of GC-MS to identify and characterize a complex mixture of organic solvents. The solvents are present at the 20-nanogram per component level.

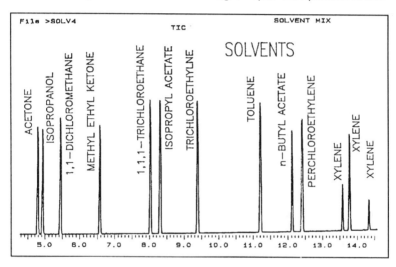

Figure 5-14. Total ion trace of a complex mixture of organic solvents using a capillary-direct interface. The chromatographic resolution is comparable to that of a flame ionization detector.

GC-MS may also be used to select and identify potentially dangerous materials from complex matrices, as shown in Figure 5-15. A sample of brandy was subjected to GC-MS analysis to determine if any ethyl carbamate was present, and if so how much? A standard of 10 nanograms of ethyl carbamate was prepared for comparison of retention time and mass spectra from both samples. As can be seen in Figure 5-15, the ethyl carbamate peak in the standard and the peak in the brandy appear to be at the same retention time. Normally, the matching retention times would have been sufficient to determine the presence of ethyl carbamate; however, the manufacturer wanted to know the absolute identity of the peak in the brandy sample at the retention time that corresponded to the ethyl carbamate. The mass spectrum from the peak in the brandy was compared to a mass spectrum from the standard. The results are shown in Figure 5-16. The mass spectra matched peak for peak, allowing a more certain identification. The manufacturer was able to eliminate the ethyl carbamate before bottling the product.

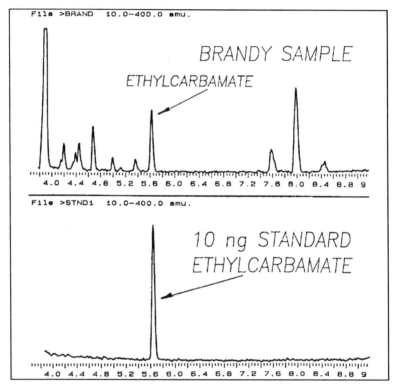

Figure 5-15. Comparison of total ion traces of a brandy sample and a 10-ng standard of ethyl carbamate by GC-MS. The minimum detection limit for ethyl carbamate was observed to be considerably less than one nanogram as demonstrated by the strong signal- to-noise ratio in the standard 10-ng trace.

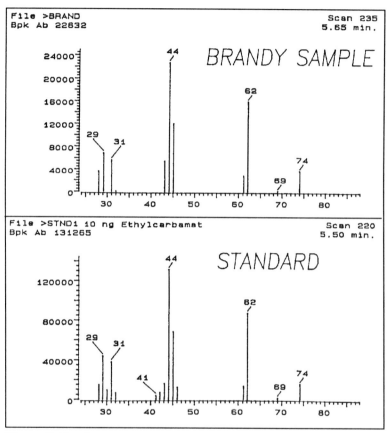

Figure 5-16. Comparison of two spectra. One mass spectrum from the peak of the suspected ethyl carbamate in the brandy and the second spectrum from the peak in the 10-ng sample. The comparison is an excellent match for the ethyl carbamate.

As can be seen from a limited number of examples, GC-MS is a powerful tool and may be applied to the analysis of almost any volatile organic complex mixture. The results can be obtained in a few minutes, which has made GC-MS the most cost-effective analytical tool available to the chemist today.

Capillary GC-IR

R. Leibrand

Combining infrared detection with high resolution gas chromatography (GC-IRD) provides a powerful tool for specific molecular information for the sample components. The molecule is vibrationally excited by infrared radiation, resulting in stretching and bending vibrations characteristic to the functional groups that comprise the molecule. Using manual interpretation or library search techniques, the spectral data generated by the infrared detector can confirm the identity of the chromatographic components.

Instrumentation for infrared analysis has been commercially available for over 40 years. The early instruments were dispersive designs that used a prism or grating to separate the infrared radiation into narrow wavelength bands that were passed sequentially through the sample. This dispersive technique is a relatively slow mechanical scanning process. By utilizing an interferometer in place of a prism or grating, modern Fourier transform infrared (FTIR) spectrometers can virtually scan the wavelength range instantaneously, thus allowing direct on-line coupling to a capillary gas chromatograph.

Basic FT-IRD Theory and Design

Figure 5-17 illustrates the optical design of an FTIR detector. With an FT-IRD, radiation from the infrared source passes into the interferometer. A beam splitter passes one beam to a moving mirror and reflects the other to a fixed mirror. Upon reflection from the fixed and moving mirrors, the light is recombined at the beam splitter. The mirrors are positioned for different path lengths so that the beams will be out of phase upon reunion, resulting in constructive and destructive interference. Figure 5-18 illustrates constructive and destructive interference for monochromatic light. The pattern of constructive and destructive interference for all the wavelengths reaching the detector is called the interferogram. An example is shown in Figure 5-19.

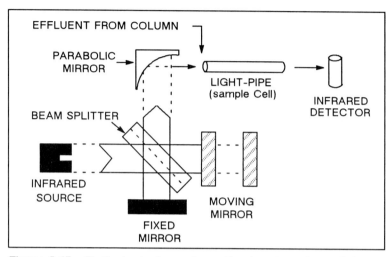

Figure 5-17. Optical design of a Fourier transform infrared detector.

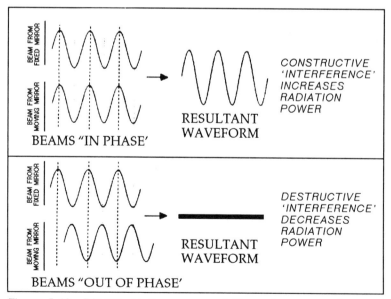

Figure 5-18. Diagrammatic representation of constructive and destructive interference for monochromatic light.

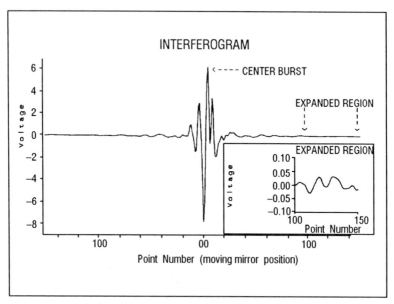

Figure 5-19. Interferogram for all infrared wavelengths.

The process for obtaining an infrared absorbance spectrum from the interferogram uses a mathematical function called the Fourier transform. The resultant chromatogram is a composite of the infrared frequencies acquired during a chromatographic run. This is referred to as the total response chromatogram (TRC) and can be compared to the total ion chromatogram (TIC) in GC-MS. Gram-Schmidt reconstruction is the technique used to transform the stored interferograms into the TRC. During a GC run, reference interferograms are mathematically compared to interferograms from the component peak resident in the light pipe. The response in the resulting Gram-Schmidt chromatogram is linear with the concentration of the sample (23).

As result of its ability to acquire full infrared spectral data rapidly, the use of an interferometer provides spectroscopic advantages over dispersive instruments.

1. *Jacquinot or optical throughput advantage* results from the ability of the interferometer to simultaneously pass all of the infrared wavelengths. The greater radiant energy at the detector leads to greater sensitivity (24) through higher signal to noise.

2. *Fellgett or multiplex advantage* also results from the simultaneous spectral acquisition accomplished with an interferometer. In comparison to dispersive instruments, a 4000–400 cm^1 infrared spectrum can be "scanned" 450 times faster. Such speed of data acquisition permits convenient signal averaging with a concomitant improvement in signal to noise. The speed of data acquisition achieved with an interferometer allows several scans to be collected across an eluting capillary GC peak that may be as narrow as only a few seconds.

3. *Connes or photometric accuracy advantage* is also achieved using an interferometer. Frequency accuracy in a dispersive instrument is limited by the reproducibility of the scanning mechanism as it moves sequentially through the range of infrared wavelengths. In contrast to this mechanical process, the interferometer uses a high-frequency laser to reference, very precisely, the system providing extremely accurate frequency assignments.

Applications

The infrared detector has tremendous power to distinguish between compounds that are structurally similar. Complimentary data is obtained from infrared spectroscopy and mass spectrometry. The combination of these two techniques provides the capability for qualitative analysis of unknown compounds with a higher confidence level. This can be illustrated in Figure 5-20 for the analysis of amphetamine and methamphetamine. The mass spectra of these two compounds are virtually identical, but distinguishable differences appear in their infrared spectra (25).

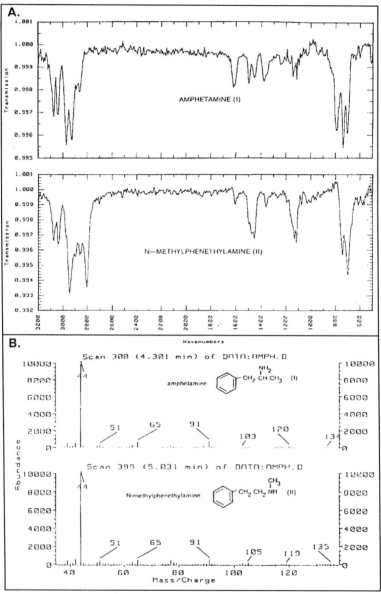

Figure 5-20. GC-IR and GC-MS analysis of amphetamine and N-methylphenethylamine. A. FTIR spectra. B. Mass spectra.

A serial configuration of infrared and mass spectral detection further strengthens the synergy of the two techniques when coupled with capillary GC. It is then possible, with a single injection, to separate the mixture with the capillary column and to acquire IR and MS data sequentially for each peak as it elutes from the column. The combination of these hyphenated techniques provides more positive compound identification, as well as the ability for convenient combined reports and library search. The use of such a combined system is illustrated in Figures 5-21 and 5-22 with a base-neutral environmental analysis (26). Note the similarity of the total response chromatogram (TRC) acquired with the IRD and the total ion chromatogram (TIC) from the MSD. The indistinguishable mass spectra of the isomers of dichlorobenzene are compared to the respective infrared spectra in Figure 5-22.

Further information on GC-FTIR, GC-FTIR-MS and their applications are included in the list of additional references at the conclusion of this chapter.

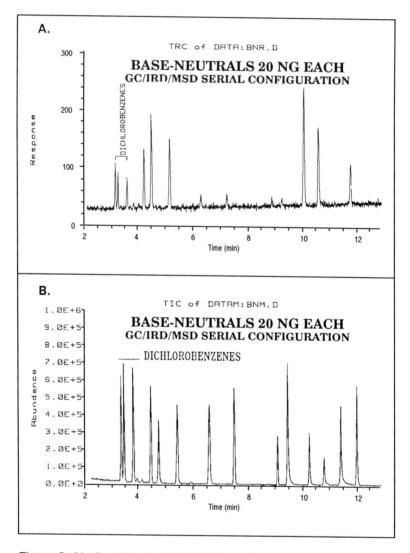

Figure 5- 21. Combined GC-IR-MS analysis of a base-neutral extract at 20 ng/component. A. Total response chromatogram (TRC), and B. Total ion chromatogram.

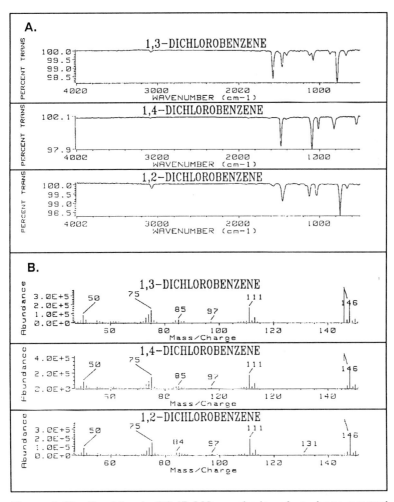

Figure 5-22. Combined GC-IR-MS analysis of a base-neutral extract. A. Infrared spectra of the dichlorobenzene isomers, and B. Mass spectra of the dichlorobenzene isomers.

References

1. Deans, D. R. 1968. *Chromatographia* 1:19–22.

2. Bertsch, W. 1978. *HRC & CC* 1:85–90.

3. Phillips, R. J., K. A. Knauss, and R. R. Freeman. 1982. *HRC & CC* 5:546–552.

4. Schomburg, G., H. Husmann, and F. Weeke. 1975. *J Chromatogr* 112: 205–217.

5. Tuinstra, L. G. M. Th., W. A. Traag, A. J. van Munsteren, and V. van Hese. 1987. *J Chromatogr* 395:307–315.

6. Schomburg, G., R. Dielmann, H. Husmann, and F. Weeke. 1976. *J Chromatogr* 122:55–72.

7. Mikkelsen, L., and S. F. Spencer. 1963. *Lectures in Gas Chromatography 1962.* Plenum Press.

8. Yoder, R., and R. Sacks. 1987. *J Chromatogr Sci* 25:21–28.

9. Chapman, J. R. 1978. *Computers in Mass Spectrometry.* London: Academic Press.

10. Watson, J. T. 1984. *Introduction to Mass Spectrometry: Biomedical, Environmental, and Forensic Applications. Second Edition.* New York: Raven Press.

11. Ettre, L. S., and W. H. McFadden. 1969. *Ancillary Techniques of Gas Chromatography.* New York: Wiley Interscience.

12. McFadden, W. H. 1973. *Techniques in Combined Gas Chromatography/Mass Spectrometry: Applications in Organic Analysis.* New York: Wiley Interscience.

13. McLafferty, F. W. 1966. *Interpretation of Mass Spectra.* New York: W.A. Benjamin.

14. Merritt, C., and C. N. McEwen. 1979. *Mass Spectrometry.* New York: Marcel Dekker Inc.

15. Budde, W. L., and J. W. Eichelberger. 1979. *Organics Analysis Using Gas Chromatography Mass Spectrometry.* Ann Arbor, Michigan: Ann Arbor Science.

16. Gross, M. L. 1978. *High Performance Mass Spectrometry: Chemical Applications.* Washington, DC: American Chemical Society.

17. Dandeneau, R., and E. H. Zerenner. 1979. *HRC & CC* 2:351–356.

18. Henneberg, D., U. Henrichs, and G. Schomburg. 1975. *Chromatographia* 8:449–451.

19. Henneberg, D., U. Henrichs, H. Husmann, and G. Schomberg. 1978. *J Chromatography* 167:139–147.

20. Koller, W. D., and G. Tressl. 1980. *HRC & CC.* 3:359–360.

21. Kenyon, C., and P. C. Goodley. 1981. *Hewlett-Packard Technical Paper No. MS-14.*

22. Leclercq, P. A., G. J. Scherpenzeel, E. A. A. Vermeer, and C. A. Cramers. 1982. *J Chromatography* 241:61–71.

23. Duncan, W. September 1987. *HP Application Note No. IRDN87-1.* Publication No. 23-5954-8185.

24. Duncan, W. December 1986. *HP IRD Note No. IRDN86-1.*

25. Duncan, W., and W. Soine. May 1986. *HP Application Note No. IRD86-2.* Publication No. 23-5954-0656.

26. Duncan, W. May 1986. *HP Application Note No. IRD86-1.* Publication No. 23-5954-0655.

Additional Reading

I. Multidimensional GC

1. Bertsch, W. 1978. *HRC & CC* 1:85–90.

2. Bertsch, W. 1978. *HRC & CC* 1:187–194.

3. Bertsch, W. 1978. *HRC & CC* 1:289–299.

4. "Special Issue: Practical Aspects of Multidimensional Gas Chromatography." 1986. *J Chromatogr Sci* 24

5. Schomburg, G. 1985. *Sample Introduction in Capillary Gas Chromatography Vol I* pp. 235–260. New York:Huethig.

6. Schomburg, G. 1987. *LC-GC* 5:304–317.

II. Hyphenated Techniques

7. Griffiths, P., and J. de Haseth. 1986. *Fourier Transform Infrared Spectroscopy. Second Edition.* New York: Wiley.

8. Griffiths, P. R., S. L. Pentoney Jr, Giorgetti and K.H. Shafer. 1986. *Anal Chem* 58:1349A–1366A.

9. Wilkens, C. L., 1987. *Anal Chem* 59:571A–581A.

10. Gurka, D., and R. Titus. 1986. *Anal Chem* 58:2189–2194.

11. Demirgian, J. C. 1987. *Trends in Anal Chem* 6:58–64.

12. Harrington, H. W., R. J. Leibrand, M. A. Hart, and W. P. Duncan. 1988. *Research & Development* (September) 82–88.

CHAPTER 6. QUALITATIVE AND QUANTITATIVE ANALYSIS
R. J. Phillips

Qualitative Analysis

Qualitative analysis involves piecing together all available information about a sample for identification of its components. Gas chromatography is especially valuable since it provides several types of information simultaneously. The appearance of the chromatogram gives an immediate indication of the complexity of the sample. Retention times allow classification of various components according to volatility. Specialized detectors, most notably the mass spectrometer, furnish elemental and structural information. Since the utility of all these techniques improves with the quality of the separation, high resolution columns greatly enhance the use of gas chromatography as a qualitative tool.

Retention Time Stability

Modern high resolution gas chromatography is characterized by extremely good precision in retention time. Much of this is due to the nature of the columns themselves. There is no packed bed to settle and, thus, no loss of permeability with age. With low thermal mass, the columns heat and cool quickly. Stationary phases are generally immobilized to prevent redistribution and reduce bleed. These improved column characteristics have stimulated manufacturers to improve instrument performance, particularly in the areas of thermal and pneumatic control. Enhanced system performance is the result.

This performance is illustrated in Table 6-1. The data are taken from a high-speed analysis of lacquer thinner using a 10 m by 100 μm id column (1). The 0.2 μl injection was split at a ratio of 1200 to 1. Oven temperature was programmed from 40° to 80°C at 30°C/min. With this demanding set of conditions, the standard deviation in retention time of approximately 30 milliseconds was measured.

Table 6-1.   Retention Time Reproducibility for Selected Peaks in
             Lacquer Thinner.

Run No. 1	Retention Time (min) 2	3	4	5	Standard Deviation
0.281	0.281	0.281	0.281	0.282	0.0004
0.551	0.550	0.550	0.550	0.551	0.0005
0.765	0.764	0.764	0.764	0.764	0.0005
1.007	1.006	1.006	1.006	1.007	0.0005
1.342	1.342	1.341	1.342	1.342	0.0004

Retention Index System

This high degree of precision in retention time has renewed
interest in the use of retention indices for peak Identification.
The retention index, as defined by Kovats (2), is a measure of
relative retention which uses the normal alkanes as a standard
reference.   Each normal hydrocarbon is assigned a number
equal to its carbon number times one hundred. For example,
n-pentane and n-decane are assigned indices of 500 and 1000,
respectively. Indices are calculated for all other compounds by
logarithmic interpolation of adjusted retention times, as shown
below in Equation 1.

$$I_a = 100N + 100n \left(\frac{\log t_{R_a}' - \log t_{R_N}'}{\log t_{R_{(N+n)}}' - \log t_{R_N}'} \right) \qquad \text{[Eq. 1]}$$

where

   N   is the carbon number of the lower n-alkane

   n   is the difference in carbon number of the two
        n-alkanes that bracket the compound

To perform the interpolation, the retention times of the
reference peaks must be known.   Often, this is done by
analyzing   a   separate   mixture   containing   only   normal
hydrocarbons. Such an analysis is shown in Figure 6-1. The

reason for using logarithmic, rather than linear interpolation, is apparent: in isothermal gas chromatography, adjusted retention times increase exponentially with carbon number.

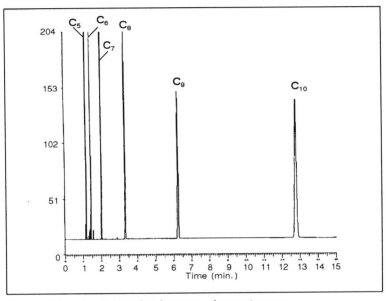

Figure 6-1. Isothermal reference chromatogram.

For this reason, temperature programming is preferred for analyses of mixtures with a wide boiling range. When linear temperature programming is used, the retention times of a homologous series increase linearly with carbon number, as shown in Figure 6-2. The concept of retention index was extended to programmed gas chromatography by Van den Dool and Kratz (3). The calculation, shown in Equation 2, is actually simplified, since the interpolation is linear, and unadjusted retention times may be used.

$$I_a = 100N + 100n \left(\frac{t_{Ra} - t_{RN}}{t_{R(N+n)} - t_{RN}} \right) \qquad \text{[Eq. 2]}$$

where

$t_{Ra}, t_{RN},$ are the retention temperatures of
and $t_{R(N+n)}$ the component and the n-alkanes
that bracket the component,
respectively.

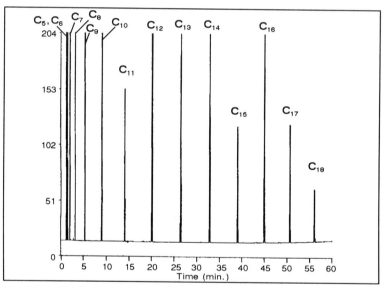

Figure 6-2.   **Programmed reference chromatogram.**

The original Kovats' (isothermal) index has the advantage of depending only on stationary phase and temperature. This simplifies the task of inter-laboratory comparison. In contrast, programmed indices require exact specification of operating conditions including column dimensions, carrier gas type, flow rate, and the temperature profile.

Once determined, the retention index can be used to help identify a compound using libraries of tabulated data. A compilation of retention indices for over 1000 flavor and fragrance volatiles has been published by Jennings and Shibamoto (4). Data were obtained on both polar (Carbowax 20M) and nonpolar (methyl silicone) stationary phases. A data base containing retention indices of 2000 compounds on four stationary phases is available commercially (5). This product is designed to work with software packages that perform calculations and that search the data base automatically.

The dual column approach (6) permits the simultaneous gathering of data on two stationary phase columns of different polarity. The advantage is greater confidence in the identification, since compounds that coelute on one of the columns may well be separated on the other. Simultaneous dual-channel data acquisition is easily accomplished using tabletop microcomputer-based workstations (7), which facilitate dual-column data analysis.

The same principle applies to the coupling of high resolution chromatography with mass spectrometry and infrared spectrometry. Results using two or more of these techniques in combination are much more reliable than those that rely on a single measurement. Thus, the recent introduction of commercial systems, which combine all three techniques, promises to have great impact on the field of organic qualitative analysis (8).

Quantitative Results

Capillary columns produce quantitative results comparable to those obtained with packed columns, as concluded from a recent collaborative study (9) conducted by the American Society for Testing and Materials. Scientists from the United States Food and Drug Administration reported similar findings, adding that, in some cases, "the higher resolving power and sensitivity attainable with capillary columns provided distinct advantages..." (10). These reports reinforce what proponents of capillary chromatography have been saying for years — that improved separation and reduced analysis time can be obtained without sacrificing quantitation.

The results obtained for a given analysis will vary, however, with the injection mode chosen. This, in turn, is dictated by the sample type and available equipment. Direct injection may be used with large diameter (0.5 mm id or larger) columns. Smaller diameter columns require more complicated injection techniques. The splitless mode is reserved for trace analysis, while split injection is used for major components. On-column injection can be used in either case, and is especially suited to compounds of low volatility.

Optimum performance with split sampling is summarized in the concept of "linearity." Linearity is the linear relationship of the system response as a function of concentration or of the amount injected (over a given range in concentration or amount). This relationship is desired for quantitation. As defined by Ettre (11), linearity includes the following:

1. Relative size of peaks must be identical to results found without splitting or to calculated results.
2. Peak area of a component must be proportional to its concentration.
3. Peak area must be proportional to sample size.
4. Peak area must be inversely proportional to split ratio.

Note that it is not necessary for the actual split ratio to equal the value calculated using the measured split and column flows. The pressure pulse that occurs during injection causes a temporary increase in column flow with a concomitant reduction in the split ratio.

Data from a linear splitter are shown in Table 6-2 (12). As shown by the ratio of nonane to hexadecane, there is no discrimination over a fairly wide boiling range. The average C_9/C_{16} ratio of 1.013 is in good agreement with the value of 1.020 $\pm$0.0062 obtained by analyzing the same sample on a packed column. The relative standard deviation for absolute peak areas is 2–3%, which is fairly typical for manual injection.

Table 6-2.   Splitter Discrimination.

Run No.	Area C_9	Area C_{16}	C_9C_{16} Ratio
1	39280	39540	0.993
2	40150	39680	1.012
3	38270	37200	1.029
4	38230	37710	1.014
5	40280	39270	1.026
6	39300	39200	1.003
Average (σ,relative)	39252 $\pm$ 880 (2.24%)	38767 $\pm$ 1043 (2.69%)	1.013 $\pm$ 0.0136 (1.34%)

In practice, perfect linearity may not always be achievable. Several guidelines can be used to obtain improved performance, however. Select a liner that is appropriate for the sample type. Liners that are tightly packed with glass wool give the best precision for hydrocarbon mixtures (13). Other designs are more appropriate for labile compounds (14). Discrimination originating within the syringe needle can be reduced by making the injection quickly (15) and by avoiding the use of highly volatile solvents (16).

Trace analysis by high resolution gas chromatography relies upon the splitless and on-column injection techniques first described by Grob (17,18). The splitless technique requires flash vaporization of the sample and, thus, exhibits molecular weight discrimination. On-column injection, done at relatively low temperatures, is superior in both precision and accuracy as shown in Table 6-3 (19). On-column injection also makes possible the analysis of heat-sensitive compounds which decompose in a heated injection port. Splitless injection has an advantage, however, because sample residues remain in the easily cleaned injection port rather than accumulating in the column as with on-column injection.

Consideration must also be given to the choice of detectors. The flame ionization detector continues to be used for the majority of applications since it combines sensitivity and linearity over a wide range of concentrations. The introduction of a low-volume, single-filament thermal conductivity detector provides a viable alternative for some applications. When used with large diameter (>0.5 mm id) columns, it offers wide dynamic range (20) and excellent precision (21).

In trace analysis, selective detectors such as the electron capture and flame photometric detectors are desirable. With careful optimization of operating parameters, these detectors exhibit extraordinary sensitivity. However, nonlinear response is generally obtained, and multilevel calibration is required for accurate results, as shown in Figure 6-3 (22).

Table 6-3.   Comparison of On-Column and Splitless injection.

| PAH | Analytical Precision at 10 ng/Component | | | | |
| | On–Column | | Splitless | | |
	Relative Response	%SD (n=6)	Relative Response	%SD (n=6)
Naphthalene	.867 ± .003	.35	.897 ± .003	.33
Biphenyl	.879 ± .004	.46	.884 ± .001	.08
Fluorene	.823 ± .002	.24	.729 ± .003	.14
C_{16}	1.00		1.00	
Phenanthrene	.914 ± .002	.22	.791 ± .014	1.77
Anthracene	.830 ± .002	.24	.696 ± .014	2.01
1–Methylanthracene	.875 ± .003	.34	.706 ± .019	2.69
Fluoranthene	.903 ± .005	.55	.697 ± .025	3.59
Pyrene	.891 ± .005	.56	.677 ± .024	3.55
2,3–Benzofluorene	.905 ± .009	.99	.582 ± .021	3.61
Triphenylene	.926 ± .009	.97	.636 ± .024	3.77
Benzo(e)pyrene	.885 ± .007	.79	.583 ± .025	4.29
Benzo(a)pyrene	.885 ± .005	.56	.531 ± .021	3.95
Piperylene	.813 ± .004	.49	.498 ± .021	4.22
1,2,5,6–Dibenzo-anthracene	.894 ± .005	.56	.421 ± .018	4.28
Coronene	.886 ± .003	.34	.375 ± .014	3.73
Average Response	.879 ± .033	3.75	.647 ± 1.52	23.5

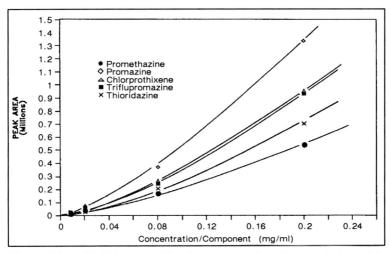

Figure 6-3. Multilevel calibration curve for flame photometric detection of antipsychotic agents.

References

1. Phillips, R. J., W. D. Snyder, and K. J. Hyver. 1987. *J Chromatogr Sci* 25:402–404.

2. Kovats, E., J. C. Giddings, and R. A. Keller. 1965. *Advances in Chromatography, Volume 1* Chapter 7. New York: Marcel Dekker.

3. Van den Dool, H., and Kratz, P. D. 1963. *J Chromatogr* 11:463–71.

4. Jennings, W., and T. Shibamoto. 1980. *Qualitative Analysis of Flavor and Fragrance Volatiles by Gas Chromatography*. New York: Academic Press.

5. Sprouse, J. F., and A. Varano. 1984. *Amer Lab* 16:54–68.

6. Phillips, R. J., *Capillary Chromatography in Essential Oil Analysis* In: P. Sandra and C. Bicchi, Eds. 1987. Chapter 9. Heidelberg: Huethig

7. Hyver, K. J. July 1987. *Hewlett-Packard Application Note No. 228-256.* HP Publication No. 43-5954-9172.

8. Borman, S. 1987. *Anal Chem* 59:769A–774A.

9. McMahon, D. H. 1985. *J Chromatogr Sci* 23:137–143.

10. Fehringer, N. V., and S. M. Walters. 1986. *J Assoc Off Anal Chem* 69:90–93.

11. Ettre, L., and W. Averill. 1961. *Anal Chem* 33:680–684.

12. Smith, D. H., P. F. Bente, R. R. Freeman, and J. E. Cusack. September 1978. *Hewlett-Packard Technical Paper No. 74* HP Publication No. 43-5953-1401.

13. Schomburg, G., H. Behlau, R. Dielmann, F. Weeke, and H. Husmann. 1977. *J Chromatogr* 142:87–102.

14. Jennings, W. G. 1975. *J Chromatogr Sci* 13:185–187.

15. Snyder, W. D. June 1985. *Hewlett-Packard Technical Paper No. 108* HP Publication No. 43-5953-1843.

16. Proske, M. G., M. Bender, G. Schomburg, and E. Hubinger. 1982. *J Chromatogr* 240:95–106.

17. Grob, K., and G. Grob. 1969. *J Chromatogr Sci* 7:584–586.

18. Grob, K., and K. Grob Jr. 1978. *J Chromatogr* 151:311–320.

19. Turner, M. P., and R. R. Freeman. November 1982. *Hewlett-Packard Application Note AN 228-28* HP Publication No. 43-5953-1679.

20. Phillips, R. J., and A. Gratzfeld-Husgen. April 1984. *Hewlett-Packard Application Note 228-38* HP Publication No. 43-5953-1770.

21. Kolloff, R. H., C. Toney, and J. Butler. August 1985. *Hewlett-Packard Technical Paper No. 110* HP Publication No. 43-5953-1878.

22. Hyver, K. J. November 1986. *Hewlett-Packard Application Note 228-51* HP Publication No. 43-5954-7614.

CHAPTER 7. SYSTEM PERFORMANCE—EVALUATION AND TROUBLESHOOTING
R. C. Gearhart

Introduction

It is important to establish overall gas chromatographic system performance before routine use of the system is initiated. This chapter serves as a general reference guide for monitoring performance as a function of time and serves as a diagnostic aid for problem solving. Readers are encouraged to refer to manufacturer's information provided with the specific chromatographic system for more detailed information on troubleshooting and performance specifications.

Many parameters can be used as measurements of overall chromatographic system performance and/or to provide "pointers" to potential problems in specific functional areas of the system (sample injection, inlet, column, detector, signal processing). Measurement parameters either overlap or duplicate each other in terms of information given about system health. In general, it is best to base conclusions about a system on as many different performance measures as is conveniently possible.

System Baseline

Baseline behavior is an often ignored but vitally important attribute of any chromatographic system. Ultimately, it defines the limit on system sensitivity (signal-to-noise ratio, "S/N") and affects reproducibility of results (signal integration processes). Baseline quality becomes increasingly important with the need for specificity and reproducibility.

A chromatographic baseline is the sum of the baselines from the following:

1. Detector and signal processing, mechanical, and electrical components.

2. A detector operating without material contributions from the analytical column.

3. Detected amounts of material from the analytical column.

In any analysis where a sample is introduced into the chromatographic system, the observed component peaks may be thought of as "riding" on top of these three summed baselines.

Baseline aberrations fall into five general categories: "spiking" (positive, negative), high noise, high wander, severe drift, and/or sudden shifts. In the case of spiking, noise, and wander, these problems may evidence themselves as periodic (occurring regularly in time), or aperiodic (randomly occurring). Various baseline problems are depicted in Figure 7-1.

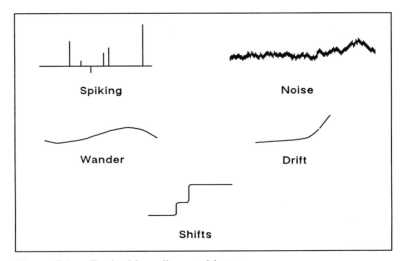

Figure 7-1. Typical baseline problems.

Any mix of these baseline aberrations can occur across any combination of the three contributing baselines; therefore, it is important to know how to look at each baseline independently in evaluating baseline behavior. The following is a guide to sources of problems affecting each contributing baseline. In troubleshooting, each baseline should be inspected in the order presented here; otherwise, conclusions can be confounded by a collection of problems spread across the several contributing baselines.

Electromechanical Baseline

Where possible, this baseline can be observed by plotting only detector signal output. This is obtained by turning the detector on electronically, but not turning on that which makes the detector functional; for example, by not igniting the flame for a flame ionization or flame photometric detector (FID or FPD), by not supplying power to the active element (bead) of a nitrogen-phosphorus detector (NPD), or by not supplying power to the filament of a thermal conductivity detector (TCD). Unfortunately, not all detector types can be operated in this nonfunctional mode.

To observe the signal adequately in the nonfunctional mode, it is usually necessary to operate signal processing electronics at the most sensitive levels, compensating for any offset as needed. Plotting should continue for at least five minutes and can be continued as long as necessary.

Since, in this mode, the detector itself is unable to respond to material passing through the system, any baseline problems observed can be related to the instrument and/or to its environment. Baseline behavior in this situation distinguishes problems in detector support electronics and signal processing areas of the system from any possible problems associated with column and sample inlet areas. Possible causes of baseline problems in this situation are given in Table 7-1.

Table 7-1.　　Troubleshooting Electromechanical Baseline
　　　　　　　Problems.

● Spiking　　Spiking is usually due to electrical disturbances
　　　　　　　through power lines or poorly shielded cables.

　　　　　　　When periodic spiking is observed, look for
　　　　　　　anything sharing the system's electrical
　　　　　　　environment cycling at the same time a spike
　　　　　　　is observed.

　　　　　　　Aperiodic spiking may also be due to electrical
　　　　　　　disturbances through power lines and signal
　　　　　　　cables as above, but from devices not cycled on
　　　　　　　a regular basis.

　　　　　　　In addition, this type of spiking can occur from
　　　　　　　problems within detector and signal processing
　　　　　　　systems, such as loose, dirty, or corroded
　　　　　　　electrical connections at junctions along the
　　　　　　　signal path detector signal pickup point,
　　　　　　　signal board connectors, cable connectors, etc.
　　　　　　　Mechanical movements caused by thermal
　　　　　　　expansion/contraction or by vibration at these
　　　　　　　poorly conducting junctions will cause spikes.

● Noise　　　Excessive observed noise is usually due to either
　　　　　　　a defective detector signal board (electrometer)
　　　　　　　or to radiated interference from some nearby
　　　　　　　piece of electronic equipment. The latter
　　　　　　　possibility can be tested by turning off nearby
　　　　　　　equipment to determine if observed noise is
　　　　　　　reduced.

● Wander　　Wander is usually caused by environmental
　　　　　　　problems such as dramatic cyclical changes in
　　　　　　　ambient temperature or line voltage. For a
　　　　　　　TCD, thermal control circuitry for the detector
　　　　　　　may be defective.

● Shifts　　　Abrupt shifts in offset are usually traced to poor
　　　　　　　connections (loose, dirty, or corroded) along
　　　　　　　signal paths. Often, by making small mechanical
　　　　　　　movements at junctions, problem points can be
　　　　　　　located and corrected.

Functional Baseline

This baseline is observed by plotting detector signal output with the detector turned on electronically and made functional without material input from an analytical column. That is, carrier and support gases are supplied to the detector at appropriate operational flow rates, the detector is heated to its operational temperature and, for example, the flame is ignited for an FID or FPD, or power is supplied to the active element (bead) of an NPD or to the filament of a TCD.

Where makeup gas is available to the detector (those designed for use with capillary columns), the detector is plugged/capped at its column fitting inside the oven; and makeup gas flow rate is set to simulate total carrier flow (column plus makeup flow rates) to the detector.

For detectors limited to packed column use, a column known to have low bleed characteristics may be installed, with the inlet and oven left in their off (unheated) states to minimize material entering the detector. Alternatively, a piece of clean tubing may be installed in place of the column (again, its temperature should be left at ambient).

As mentioned before, to observe the signal adequately in this state, it is usually necessary to operate signal processing electronics at the most sensitive levels, compensating for any offset as needed. Plotting should continue for at least five minutes and can be continued as long as necessary.

Since, in this mode, the detector has virtually no material passing through to which it can respond, any baseline problems observed can be related to the detector and its support systems (gas supplies, etc.). Again, this diagnostic mode distinguishes detector-related problems from those related to the inlet or column. Various possible causes of functional baseline problems are presented in Table 7-2.

Table 7-2.   Troubleshooting Functional Detector Baseline
             Problems.

● Spiking   Aperiodic spiking is often due to particulate
            matter passing through the active part of
            the detector; the detector requires cleaning;
            and/or matter is being carried in through
            support gases.

            Periodic spiking is rare but may occur where
            detector operation requires a mechanical
            pneumatic switching valve, such as in certain
            TCD designs. Since the valve is switched at a
            constant frequency, if its mechanical action is
            defective, flow switching is disturbed, often
            periodically. In this situation, the time interval
            between spikes generally wil be some integer
            multiple of the valve cycling rate.

            Another cause of periodic spiking may be due
            to "burping" elastomeric seals (e.g., O-rings)
            in support gas plumbing. Pressure may build to
            a level where gas momentarily escapes past a
            seal, thereby relieving the excess pressure. This
            process continues in regular cycles of pressure
            buildup and release. Each time this occurs, flow
            rate to the detector is disturbed, often causing a
            spike. As a diagnostic for this situation, the time
            interval between spikes will be pressure-dependent.

● Noise   Cause for excessive observed noise varies with
            detector type; for each example, air leakage into a
            TCD or ECD system or incorrect air/hydrogen
            mixture in an FID or NPD. Mechanical defects such
            as a bad jet in an FID, NPD, or FPD also can be a
            cause of increased noise. Additionally, air currents
            passing over the exhaust vent of a detector can
            often increase noise level.

● Offset   Since the observed baseline is simply detector offset
            plotted over time, the absolute offset level is of
            interest in itself—even if constant, excessive offset
            compresses the usable dynamic range of the
            detector.

            High offset problems are detector-specific: incorrect
            gas mixtures and/or flow rates, contaminated
            supply gases, air leakage into a TCD or ECD,
            excessive current to the bead of an NPD, excessive
            voltage to the photomultiplier of an FPD, etc.

continued

Table 7-2.   Troubleshooting Functional Detector Baseline
            Problems (cont).

● Wander   For any detector type, wander is often caused by
           poor flow rate control of support gases (for
           example, cycling of a compressor supplying air to
           an FID). Other cases are specific to detector type:
           poor thermal stability for a TCD, poor current
           regulation for the active element in an NPD, poor
           voltage control for a photomultiplier tube in an
           FPD, etc.

● Drift   Gradual downward drift in the baseline is usually
           due to the "bake-out" of chemical contaminants
           within the detector, and/or purging of contami-
           nants from support gas plumbing.

           Upward drift in this situation is unusual, but if
           observed, may be due to drift of support gas
           flow rates, or detector-specific causes such as
           drifting NPD bead current.

Chromatographic Baseline

This baseline is observed during one or more blank runs; that
is, with the analytical column installed and with all gas flow
rates and temperatures set to the values to be used for the
selected analysis, normal chromatographic runs are made with
no sample introduction. In this mode, the baseline is affected
mainly by material eluting from inlet plumbing and/or the
column.

Again, to observe the signal adequately in this state, it is
usually necessary to operate signal processing electronics at
the most sensitive levels, compensating for any offset as
needed, with plot attenuation adjusted so the entire plot
remains on-scale. Plotting should continue for the length of the
run.

With the chromatographic system set up and operating in a manner comparable to that necessary for performing the analysis, potential baseline irregularities can be determined. Possible causes of baseline problems are shown in Table 7-3.

Table 7-3.   Troubleshooting Chromatographic Baseline Problems.

● Offset   Since the observed baseline is simply detector offset plotted over time, the absolute offset level is of interest in itself; even if constant, excessive offset compresses usable dynamic range for the detector.

High offset problems in this mode are usually due to elution of material from the inlet system (contamination) and/or from the analytical column (contamination or bleed from the stationary phase).

Generally, offset will be a function of temperature, with higher temperature resulting in higher offset. Thus, inlet-related problems can be distinguished from column-related problems simply by changing the temperature of each instrument zone independently to determine which has the greater effect on the observed offset.

● Wander For an isothermal system, wander is usually the result of things such as contaminated carrier gas or poor carrier gas flow rate control. In addition, for a temperature-programmed system, amounts of material eluting from the column itself may not increase in a uniform manner with temperature.

● Drift   Gradual upward drift in the baseline is usually expected in temperature-programmed situations, since column bleed typically increases along with column temperature.

In an isothermal situation, drift is not expected. If observed, it is most likely due to drift in one or more of the underlying baselines discussed above.

continued

Table 7-3.   Troubleshooting Chromatographic Baseline
             Problems (cont).

● "Ghost" Peaks Peaks observed when there is no sample
                 introduced into the system are usually
                 due to contaminating materials in the
                 inlet or column (e.g., leftover sample
                 material from previous analyses). Such
                 peaks are most likely to occur when
                 switching to an analytical method requir-
                 ing higher inlet or column temperatures,
                 thus driving off materials accumulated
                 during the cooler analysis.

                 Another common source of such peaks is
                 bleed from the inlet septum or from broken
                 pieces of septum material lodged within the
                 inlet body and/or liner. Thorough cleaning
                 of the inlet and replacement of the inlet
                 liner and septum is required.

                 For the column, the inlet end may be
                 contaminated with thermal degradation
                 products and/or poorly volatilized
                 material. For a fused silica capillary column,
                 there may be exposed pieces of protective
                 polyimide coating at either end of the
                 column. Column ends should be carefully
                 inspected, and affected sections cut off if
                 possible.

                 For some capillary columns, after cutting
                 off visibly contaminated sections, the
                 column may then be rinsed (following
                 manufacturer's instructions) and finally
                 conditioned at a temperature somewhat in
                 excess of the maximum to be used for the
                 analysis, but within the temperature
                 range specified by the manufacturer.

Summary: Baseline Behavior

As a final note, it is important that the overall chromatographic baseline be as drift-free and wander-free as is possible (e.g., essentially horizontal over the course of the run). This will ensure that peaks have their start and end points sharply and symmetrically defined to ensure the best possible quantitative interpretation (measured peak area).

When trace-level analyses are to be performed, it is also important to have the least amount of noise possible in the baseline to minimize the possibility of noise hiding peak information.

For baseline drift and wander, some systems offer electronic column compensation, whereby a blank baseline profile is stored and then later subtracted from the analytical chromatographic run, thus flattening its baseline. In using electronic column compensation, one should be aware that noise is INCREASED in the compensated baseline. Since noise is random, the variance in the stored baseline profile is added to that in the analytical run. Thus, in trace-level analyses, column compensation may not be advisable.

Peak Shape Problems

Ideally, one expects a chromatographic peak to appear both symmetric and Gaussian, and to have a well-defined start, end, and top. As peak shape becomes further removed from this expectation, interpretation of its features (area, height, and retention time) becomes increasingly more difficult (whether by manual or electronic integration methods) and, therefore, more subject to error.

In this section, an ideal (horizontal and noise-free) baseline will be assumed. Typical peak shape aberrations and the most-likely causes will be discussed. Various peak shape problems are illustrated in Figure 7-2.

Any mix of these problems can occur in a given analysis. The following is a guide to sources of problems affecting peak shape, along with troubleshooting information.

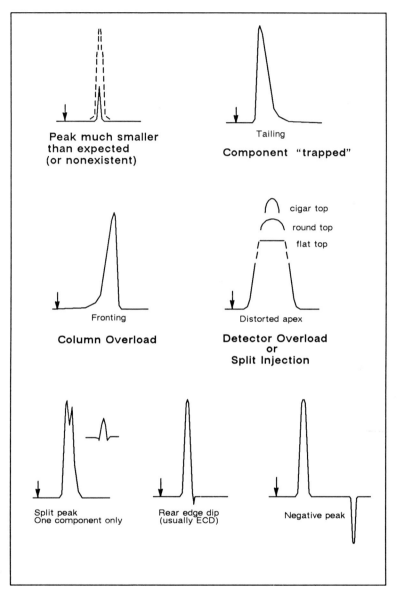

Figure 7-2.   Typical peak shape problems.

Little or No Peak Response

Two different problem situations are included here. The first is absolutely no peaks appearing in an analytical run, including response from a solvent and/or other components in highest concentration. The second is no detected response from components in the highest concentration and from components in lesser concentrations.

In troubleshooting, it is good practice to have on hand a "checkout" sample available as an independent test of system performance. Ideally, the sample should be of known components representative of those expected in the samples being analyzed. Component concentrations should also be known and high enough to ensure detectability. Where the analyses require a calibration sample for peak identification, the calibration sample itself often will serve as a checkout sample.

Various possible causes of problems in these situations, presented in order of sample introduction through signal processing, are listed in Table 7-4.

Table 7-4.   Troubleshooting Poor Peak Response Problems.

● Injector   A number of syringe-related problems are possible, such as a clogged needle and/or serious leakage between plunger and barrel. In an automated injection system the syringe needle may be damaged. For an automated injection system one should also check mechanisms driving the plunger and syringe into the sample vial as well as into the chromatograph inlet. Also, verify that the sample level in the vial is sufficient to ensure immersion of the syringe needle when the sample is being drawn into the syringe. If a problem with an automated injector is suspected, manual injection may be performed for verification.

continued

Table 7-4. Troubleshooting Poor Peak Response Problems (cont).

● Inlet	At the inlet, most-likely problems include gross leakage (e.g., a "blown" septum or defective column ferrule) or lack of carrier gas flow. For a split mode capillary inlet, the split ratio may be far too high; for a splitless mode capillary inlet, perhaps the inlet is being purged too soon. For inlets dependent upon flash vaporization, inlet temperature may be too low. For a cool on-column inlet, the column may not be installed correctly so that the sample is not introduced into the column.
● Column	The column must be installed according to instructions given by the manufacturer of the chromatograph. It should be checked for possible blockage by verifying carrier flow at the detector. Also, verify that no leakage exists at inlet or detector ends. For glass or fused silica columns, check that the column is not fractured.
● Detector	Ensure that the detector is functional (e.g., an FID has its flame lit) and electronically enabled. For a multiple detector system, verify that detector output is correctly assigned to the signal processing system. Also, verify that the detector's electrometer offset (zero) adjustment is set properly, ensuring a small positive output voltage to signal processing electronics.
● Signal Processing	Verify that the signal cable is connected properly and that signal attenuation settings are reasonable for expected sample component concentrations.

"Trapped" Peak Response

Discrete chemical components may be "trapped" by one or more of several mechanisms: (i) mechanical trapping whereby material is caught in regions poorly swept by carrier gas, (ii) cold trapping whereby material condenses in poorly heated regions, and (iii) chemical trapping whereby material is caught in areas having chemical affinity for the material.

Although the mechanisms are distinctly different, all three cause "tailing" of affected component peaks and/or loss of response (loss of area and height). Often, the effect is independent of sample volume injected. The effect is typically discriminatory, affecting some components more than others based upon relative chemical reactivities, boiling points, etc. Troubleshooting possibilities, organized in order of sample introduction through detection, are presented in Table 7-5.

In summary, choosing the appropriate stationary phase for the column, maintaining cleanliness, and following the manufacturer's recommendations for column installation and use of parts are the most important items in minimizing component trapping problems. Additional care not to make alterations that will affect thermal behavior, internal volumes, and flow paths, and careful selection of operating temperatures are secondary considerations.

Table 7-5.   Troubleshooting "trapped" Peak Problems.

> ● Inlet   At the inlet, with respect to chemical trapping, it is essential to have all components, through which sample passes, as chromatographically clean as possible.
>
> To minimize unswept volume problems, it is essential to follow manufacturer's recommendations concerning column installation and choice of consumable and replacement parts. Modification of an inlet or its component parts is generally not a good idea.
>
> For inlets dependent upon flash vaporization, cold-trapping of components may occur simply due to too low an operating temperature or to technical problems, such as insufficient or poorly distributed insulation or removal of heat-retaining covers. There can also be cold-trapping problems where the inlet passes into the oven, particularly when the oven is being operated at a much lower temperature than the inlet.

continued

Table 7-5.   Troubleshooting "trapped" Peak Problems (cont).

● Column	With respect to chemical trapping, choice of stationary phase must be appropriate for the chemical class of components to be separated. Incorrect matching can lead to cases of near-permanent absorption of material by the stationary phase.
● Detector	Like the inlet, the detector must be kept chromatographically clean , and column install-ation and use of consumable or replacement parts must follow manufacturer recommendations. Also, operating temperature must be sufficient to ensure that no cold-trapping occurs.

Overloaded Peak Response

Overload situations may occur for components in relatively high concentrations causing saturation problems in the inlet, column, detector, and/or signal processing electronics. The effect on peak shape depends upon the part of the system in which saturation occurs.

Possible peak shape problems for saturation conditions, organized in order from sample introduction through signal processing, are presented in Table 7-6.

In summary it should be noted that overload situations should be avoided, if at all possible, since peaks can be affected and yield corrupt feature information (retention time, area, and/or height). This is particularly true for detector and signal-processing electronics overload, as information is irretrievably lost.

Table 7-6.   Troubleshooting Peak Overload Problems.

● Inlet   Overloading the inlet generally yields peaks exhibiting extreme "tailing." Excess material is backed into poorly swept regions within the inlet. The material elutes slowly from these regions, causing extended tails on peaks associated with the materials in excess.

In troubleshooting possible inlet overload, note that only components in very high concentration should be affected, and observed tailing on the resultant very large peaks should show itself to be a function of injection volume. If possible, injected volume should be reduced.

● Column   Column overload yields peaks exhibiting "fronting" (e.g., a peak whose foreslope is not as steep as its backslope). The effect should show itself to be a function of injection volume. If possible, injected volume should be reduced.

Alternatively, if peak resolution is not a concern, a column having greater capacity (thicker stationary phase coating) should be tried.

● Detector   Detector overload can evidence itself either as a large peak with a broad rounded top or as a large peak with one or more false valleys. The former peak shape occurs as detector response becomes severely nonlinear. The latter shape occurs when the detector is temporarily "blinded" by the large amount of material passing through (e.g., temporary carbonization of an NPD-active element).

Such problems become increasingly severe the smaller the inherent dynamic range of the detector. If possible, smaller injection volumes should be tried. Alternatively, if possible, more dilute concentrations should be used.

continued

Table 7-6.   Troubleshooting Peak Overload Problems (cont).

● Signal Processing Generally, when detector output exceeds input capacity for signal processing electronics, affected peaks are "clipped," appearing as peaks with perfectly flat tops. If possible, detector output should be attenuated sufficiently to ensure that even the largest peaks anticipated will produce output levels within limits required by signal-processing electronics.

Since overload is often unavoidable for a solvent making up a given sample, avoid including solvent peak area/height in quantitative calculations. Solvent overload exhibits poor reproducibility, making it even more important that the peak area/height not be included in quantitative calculations.

Split Peak Response

As mentioned previously, where a component is in very high concentration, it may appear as a pair of overlapped peaks due to a false valley caused by detector overload. Peak splitting may also be caused by sample injection problems.

Ideally, sample is delivered into the inlet as a single band whose dimension in time (band width) is as small as possible. This requires smooth, continuous sample delivery by the injection mechanism, whether manual or mechanical. When this is not accomplished, the sample enters the column as two or more separate bands displaced one from the other in time, and results in split peaks.

The splitting occurs for all component peaks, regardless of their relative concentrations. However, it becomes increasingly pronounced with retention time and occurs for any injected sample (again, a good reason to have a well-behaved, known "checkout" sample available as a troubleshooting aid).

Analytical results where this problem occurs are corrupt, as peak widths and/or areas will be affected. The cause of this problem is often the syringe plunger (or valve rotor in a valved injection system) which has locations along its travel path where binding occurs. In automated systems, the injector mechanism may be binding. For manual injection, proper technique must be practiced as necessary.

Inverted (Negative) Peak Response

Inverted peaks are usually the result of reversed signal processing polarity. This could be due to a TCD with reversed signal polarity definition or the inadvertent miswiring of a signal cable.

There are also a few chromatographic situations where inverted peaks may occur.

    i. sample component having greater thermal conductivity than that of the carrier gas

    ii. mismatched baseline column compensation

    iii. momentary detector overload

    iv. incorrect "zeroing" of a detector electrometer output or signal processing electronics

    v. chemically active site(s) within a TCD

Negative peaks often corrupt analytical data by affecting baseline decisions and even by stealing area from legitimate component peaks at the same retention time. At a minimum, it is difficult to obtain good run-to-run reproducibility when negative peaks are present. Causes of negative peaks are described in detail in Table 7-7.

Table 7-7.   Inverted Peak Response Problems.

● Column
Compensation

When used, column compensation, whether by matched column and detector pairs or electronic, can cause negative (and positive) peaks when reference and analytical baselines are badly mismatched.

Proof that this problem exists is obtained simply by performing a blank run (no sample injected) using column compensation. Ideally, the resultant baseline should be flat. If peaks or other aberrations, such as baseline drift and/or wander, are observed, steps should be taken to correct the situation so these problems won't corrupt analytical run data.

● Detector Overload

For element-specific detectors such as ECD, NPD, FPD, etc., the baseline may be badly disturbed (both positive and negative peaks) when a component to which the detector is "blinded" passes through in high concentration (for example, the solvent) due to the detector being completely saturated by the component.

Since this is an unavoidable situation, one should attempt to have components of interest well separated in retention time from the solvent or other components in very high concentration.

continued

Table 7-7.   Inverted Peak Response Problems (cont).

• Signal Zeroing	"Zeroing" of the signal, whether at the detector output or at the signal processing system, is ideally done when the signal represents only the chromatographic background (e.g., no sample components eluting from the column). If zeroing is done while sample from a previous run is eluting from the column, the current analytical run is likely to exhibit negative baseline drift, wander, and even peaks.
	If necessary, the chromatographic system should be "baked out" periodically at high temperature to drive off accumulated strongly retained components.
• Chemical Activity	Peculiar to a TCD, negative peaks may occur when sample components react with chemically active sites within the detector. Heat changes caused by these reactions are often exhibited as negative peaks.
	If this situation is suspected, the active sites may often be passivated by repeated injections of components (in high concentration) whose chemical natures are similar to those known to be causing the observed negative peaks.

Summary: Peak Shape Behavior

For the best possible results from the chromatographic system, particularly where precise and repeatable quantitative information (peak area or height) is required, it is important that peak shape be as close to ideal as possible. This requires close attention to column choice, absence of leaks, proper column installation, injection volume, sample component concentrations, appropriate temperatures and other operating conditions.

Column Connectors

A column connector may be defined as any mechanical device used to couple two columns together. Reasons for joining columns together are varied and include:

- To repair a broken expensive analytical column.

- To "tune" stationary phase polarity by connecting sections of columns of different stationary phases.

- To connect columns of different outer diameters; that is, connecting an analytical column to a transfer line, retention gap, or replaceable precolumn.

Because column integrity is disrupted at the junction of the column ends, connector design must have minimal effect on chromatographic quality. When selecting a connector, attention should be paid to criteria given in Table 7-8.

Table 7-8.   Troubleshooting Column Connector Problems.

● Unswept Volume	The manner in which column ends are sealed by the connector may leave poorly swept voids which may trap passing components, causing tailing.
● Ferrule Exposure	Exposure of sample to ferrules used by the connector should be minimal, as ferrule materials are often chemically active, particularly at elevated temperature. Sample components may be altered chemically or absorbed by exposed ferrule material.
● Thermal Mass	For capillary columns, a connector may have far greater thermal mass than the column. Where high oven program rates are being used or where rapid oven cool-down and recycling to readiness for the next analysis is expected, the connector may lag in temperature causing a hot or cold spot.

Regardless of the connector selected, it is essential to follow the manufacturer's recommendations with respect to column installation and choice of replacement parts, such as ferrules. Improper installation of column ends will almost always result in problems (leakage, severe tailing, loss of response for certain components, difficulties in installation, etc.).

It is also important to prepare column ends to be joined properly. Ends must be cut square and free of burrs, chips of material, etc. Directions for proper preparation of column ends prior to installation should be provided by the manufacturer.

Additional Reading

1. Hewlett-Packard. 1970. *Logical Troubleshooting in Gas Chromatography* Publication No. 43-5950-8211.

2. Hyver, K. J., R. L. Dillard, R. C. Gearhart, and B. L. Ryder. October 1985. *HP Technical Paper No. 112* Publication No. 43-5953-1896.

3. Dillard, R. L., and R. C. Gearhart. April 1986. *HP Application Note 228-46* Publication No. 43-5954-7577.

4. Hinshaw, J. 1987. *LC-GC* 5:790–794.

5. Hinshaw, J. 1987. *LC-GC* 5:954–960.

6. Hinshaw, J. 1988. *LC-GC* 6:24–29.

7. Ibid 228–231.

8. Ibid 794–798.

CHAPTER 8. PRACTICAL APPLICATIONS
W. J. Sanders

With advances in column technology and instrumentation over the past decade, high resolution gas chromatography has evolved into a practical and widely used technique. Applications for capillary gas chromatography extend into nearly every industrial market. Most capillary GC applications are limited only by the molecular weight and thermal stability of the sample components. Various chemical matrices can be analyzed using a variety of sample introduction techniques.

In this chapter, applications of high resolution gas chromatography are presented which provide solutions in major segments of industry and research including: chemical, petrochemical, pharmaceutical, life sciences, food and consumer products, and environmental analyses.

Applications in the Chemical and Petrochemical Industry

This industry can be segmented into three areas—raw materials, processed petroleum products, and chemicals—as shown in Figure 8-1. The following applications illustrate some of the more common uses of fused silica open tubular columns in the petroleum/chemical industry.

Simulated Distillation

Simulated distillation is an analytical technique widely used to obtain the boiling point distribution of petroleum fractions by gas chromatography (1,2). Chromatographic simulated distillation has decided advantages over vacuum distillation (ASTM Standard D-1160) and the 15/5 true boiling point analysis (ASTM Standard D-2892). Simulated distillation by gas chromatography (ASTM Standard D-2887) for the analysis of petroleum products is not only faster and more precise, but requires smaller sample sizes.

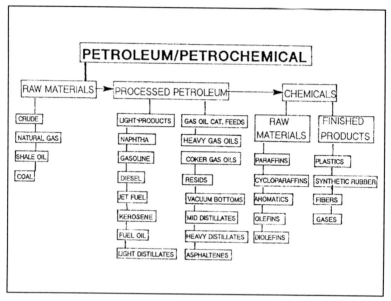

Figure 8-1. Petroleum/petrochemical raw material segmentation.

The traditional GC simulated distillation method (ASTM D-2887) is a packed column method. The recent economics surrounding the production of heavy crude oils has driven this traditional GC method for simulated distillation to its chromatographic limits. In addition, most petroleum refineries prefer to characterize the light and heavy petroleum fractions (C_1 to C_{120}) using the same technique on a single instrument. This cannot be accomplished using packed column methods.

Firor (3) has shown the practical advantages of using capillary columns in comparison to packed columns for chromatographic simulated distillation.

Using a gas chromatograph, equipped with a high temperature oven, on-column inlet and a wide bore fused silica column coated with cross-linked methylsilicone, the characterization of petroleum heavy distillates was achieved accurately, as shown in Figure 8-2. The gas chromatography conditions for this application are shown in Table 8-1. The capillary system has two decided advantages over the packed method. First, the on-column inlet eliminates the degradation of thermally labile compounds and inlet discrimination. Second, the capillary column can be customized for simulated distillation applications (Table 8-2). With one method, light, as well as heavy distillates with boiling points above 750°C, can be analyzed by capillary GC, as shown in Figure 8-3.

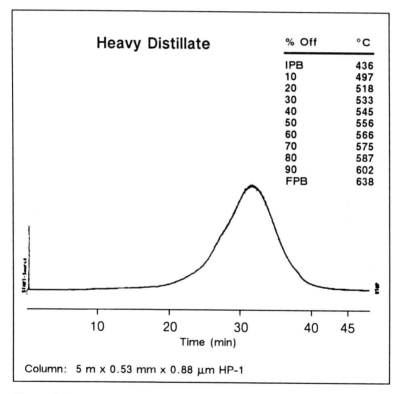

Heavy Distillate	% Off	°C
	IPB	436
	10	497
	20	518
	30	533
	40	545
	50	556
	60	566
	70	575
	80	587
	90	602
	FPB	638

Time (min)

Column: 5 m x 0.53 mm x 0.88 μm HP-1

Figure 8-2. Chromatogram and simulated distillation results for a heavy distillate. Oven temperature profile: 35°C programmed to 400°C at 10°C/min with 10 min hold.

Table 8-1.   GC Operating Conditions for High Temperature Simulated Distillation.

Typical Oven Program		System Calibration	
Initial Temp	40°C	Standard	Polywax 655
Initial Time	0 min	Calibration Range	Approximate C_{14}–C_{100}
Program Rate	6°C/min	Solvent	CS_2 or Toluene
Final Temperature	430°C	Concentration	8 g/l
Final Time	5 min	Frequency	1 or 2 times/day
Equilibration Time	8 min		
Column: 5 m x 0.53 mm x 0.1 μm cross-linked methyl silicone			

Table 8-2.   Capillary Column Simulated Distillation Methods.

Column Dimension	Method	Sample Matrix
5 m x 0.53 mm x 0.25 μm	D-2887/Ext .D-2887	Crude oils
15 m x 0.53 mm x 0.88 μm	Lights + Ext .D-2887	Lights/Crudes
30 m x 0.53 mm x 5.0 μm	D-3710	Gasoline
5 m x 0.53 mm x 0.1 μm	High Temperature	Heavy Crudes

The characterization of heavy petroleum fractions, such as heavy crude oils, residuals, and asphaltines, can be accomplished using a thin-film 5 m x 0.53 mm fused silica column with a high temperature polyimide or aluminum protective coating.   The Polywax 655 with added C_{12}–C_{18} n-paraffins provides an ideal calibration standard for this application as shown in Figure 8-3.   A high temperature simulated distillation calibration curve for Polywax 655 (Figure 8-4) relates retention time to the boiling point for C_{14} to C_{108} hydrocarbons.

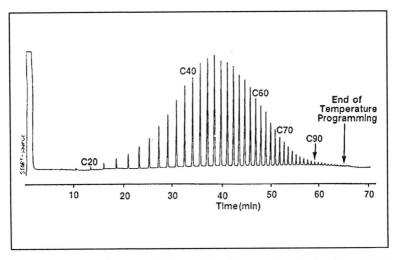

Figure 8-3. Polywax 655 calibration standard for high temperature simulated distillation. Conditions given in Table 8-1.

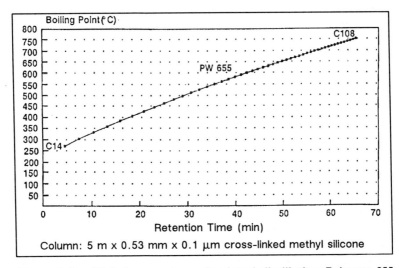

Figure 8-4. High temperature simulated distillation Polywax 655 calibration.

Hydrocarbon-Type Analyses—PNA, PONA, and PIONA*

In refining petroleum, it is highly important to determine hydrocarbon types for the naphthas and gasoline blending stocks. The standard method, used routinely for over 25 years, is the fluorescent indicator adsorption (FIA) method (ASTM D1319) (4). This method does not provide naphthene (cycloparaffin) content or specific compound identification and is subject to a high degree of human error. A high resolution mass spectrometer method (ASTM D2789) (5) has been used to give a more detailed analysis, including the determination of naphthenes. However, this method based on magnetic sector mass spectrometers is not cost-effective for routine analysis.

Currently, two approaches are being used for hydrocarbon-type analysis by high resolution gas chromatography. Methods using either a single capillary column or multidimensional analysis have been developed. Applications of the two HR-GC methods are discussed in this chapter as well as in a recent paper by Di Sanzo and Giarrocco (6). Advantages and limitations of the two systems are discussed and compared to the standard mass spectrometry method.

Sadtler (7) developed a single-column approach to PNA analysis using a DC-550 SCOT column and a custom software package. This single-column approach inspired Green and Matt (8) to develop a method using a high-efficiency, thick-film fused silica WCOT for PNA analysis. Isomer separations can be made on a 50 m x 0.2 mm column coated with a 0.5 μm film of cross-linked methylsilicone. The capillary system can be calibrated by analyzing standard mixtures containing either 103 or 215 saturates and aromatics. Gas chromatography conditions are optimized to give the most efficient separation of C_3 to C_{11} components.

---

* Commonly used abbreviations for the various methods of hydrocarbon-type analysis. PNA—paraffins, naphthenes, and aromatics. PONA—includes olefins. PIONA—includes olefins and isoparaffins.

A typical chromatogram of a petroleum naphtha sample is shown in Figure 8-5. A summary of the repeatability of the method for multiple analyses of four different petroleum samples is given in Table 8-3. The accuracy of the high resolution GC method is compared to the standard mass spectrometry method in Table 8-4.

Table 8-3.   Precision of PNA Analysis.

| Sample | VOL% | | | | | | | |
	Light Naphtha M(6)	σ	Heavy Naphtha M(5)	σ	S.R. Naphtha M(6)	σ	Reformate M(5)	σ
Total P	70.24	0.12	60.98	0.20	57.93	0.12	12.14	0.13
Total N	15.72	0.05	10.51	0.23	25.61	0.14	12.15	0.03
Total A	14.04	0.11	28.51	0.17	16.46	0.03	75.72	0.11
P3-5	2.22	0.04	0.00	0.00	0.92	0.009	0.00	0.00
P6	17.26	0.20	0.07	0.004	2.45	0.008	0.68	0.03
P7	13.63	0.09	0.21	0.007	6.39	0.013	3.28	0.07
P8	16.19	0.14	0.55	0.01	13.66	0.12	2.93	0.02
P9+	20.94	0.41	60.15	0.20	34.56	0.08	5.24	0.15
N5	0.50	0.008	0.00	0.00	0.06	0.00	0.00	0.00
N6	2.85	0.03	0.00	0.00	1.89	0.008	0.03	0.004
N7	4.06	0.02	0.13	0.004	7.99	0.02	1.64	0.05
N8	3.88	0.04	0.26	0.017	8.40	0.03	0.02	0.015
N9+	4.42	0.04	10.12	0.25	7.28	0.15	10.44	0.08
A6	0.90	0.03	0.07	0.004	0.60	0.005	0.86	0.03
A7	2.96	0.06	0.53	0.017	3.92	0.02	17.71	0.17
A8	4.14	0.03	2.47	0.14	5.88	0.02	31.13	0.11
A9+	6.04	0.15	25.44	0.18	6.05	0.04	26.00	0.16

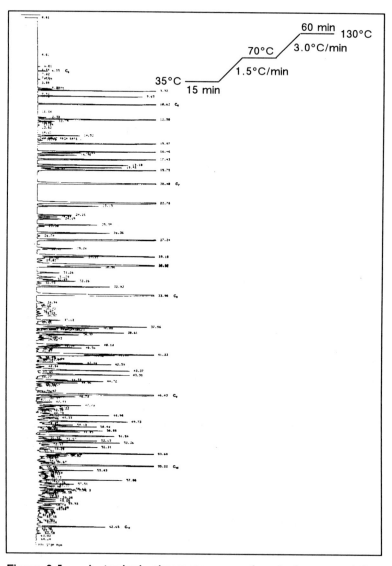

Figure 8-5.   A typical chromatogram of petroleum naphtha. Column: 0.20 mm x 50 m x 0.5 μm cross-linked methyl silicone FSWCOT.   Carrier gas: helium, 20 cm/s. Sample: 1 μl @ 400:1 split ratio. Injection temp: 250°C. Detector temp: 300°C.

Table 8-4.   Comparison of PNA Analysis Methods.

	VOL%			
	Naphtha 1		Naphtha 2	
Method	HP	MS Type(a)	HP	MS Type(a)
Total P	52.20	53.62	54.60	53.6
Total N	32.46	31.34	34.68	35.5
Total A	15.35	14.54	10.71	10.9

a) Mass Spectrometer-Type Analysis by ASTM D2789—Samples 1 and 2 by different laboratories

Analytical Controls (Delft, Holland) has developed a versatile, automated GC system that allows the determination of PNA, PONA, or PIONA. This system is a complex multicolumn and valve GC with oven-mounted valves and is reported to have very good precision. Green and Naizhong (9) developed a new approach to the determination of hydrocarbon types in petroleum naphthas using special PLOT columns and a single valve to give a rapid analysis. A schematic diagram of the system is shown in Figure 8-6. Stainless steel tubing (1.6 mm od x 0.38 mm id) was used for all connecting lines. The precolumn is mounted in a special heated box controlled by an auxiliary heater at 430°C, which was placed in the GC oven with the analytical column. The analytical column is a 7.2 m PLOT molecular sieve 13X modified with potassium hydroxide. The precolumn is a 1.6 m column of molecular sieve 13X exchanged with manganese. The columns are conditioned by temperature programming to 450°C.

To elute the sample components from the highly adsorptive PLOT columns, the gas chromatograph is modified for oven temperature operation over 450°C. Sample (1 μl) is automatically injected through the standard split interface with 75:1 split ratio onto the precolumn. To minimize head pressure, either hydrogen or helium is used as the carrier gas. The saturates are rapidly eluted by the precolumn and pass onto the analytical column where separation occurs. Just prior to the elution of benzene from the precolumn, the valve is switched "ON," and the aromatics are backflushed as a single peak into the FID as separation of the saturates continues on the analytical column.

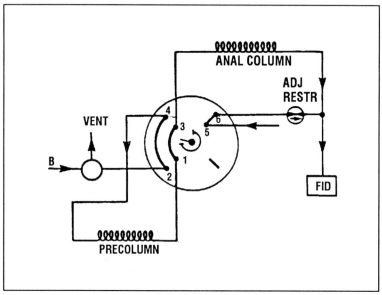

Figure 8-6.   Schematic diagram of MD-GC naphtha analysis using capillary columns.

A typical chromatogram of naphtha is shown in Figure 8-7. The naphthenes are well resolved from the paraffins with sufficient resolution between isoparaffins and n-paraffins in each carbon number through C_{12}. Analysis time is only 15 minutes. A comparison of the data obtained by this method with that of the AC system and the WCOT single column method is shown in Table 8-5.

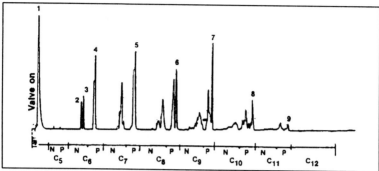

Figure 8-7.   Chromatogram of naphtha analysis. Precolumn temperature: 430°C; 13 x MS PLOT column temperature: 160°-250°C, 20°C/min. Carrier gas: hydrogen (A) 4.5 ml/min, (B) 4.5 ml/min. (1) total aromatics (2) cyclohexane, (3) methyl cyclopentane (4) n-hexane, (5) n-heptane, (6) n-octane, (7) n-nonane, (8) n-decane, (9) n-undecane. Sample size 0.16 µl. Split ratio 20:1.

Table 8-5.   Comparison of Methods for Hydrocarbon-Type Analysis of Petroleum Samples.

Sample Method	Reformer Feed		wt%	Reformate		
	PNA (WCOT)	A. C. Analyzer	PLOT	PNA (WCOT)	A.C. Analyzer	PLOT
Total NP	26.71	23.84	26.69	15.02	13.44	15.26
Total iP	30.50	31.34	29.47	33.31	32.78	31.84
Total N	25.57	29.77	28.12	5.57	3.89	3.68
Total A	17.26	15.06	15.75	46.13	49.87	49.25
C_5N	0.10	0.10	0.12	—	0.10	0.12
C_5P	0.16	0.05	0.14	2.01	1.56	1.75
C_6N	4.40	3.78	4.12	1.51	1.40	1.42
C_6iP	5.43	4.46	4.40	8.38	7.37	7.53
C_6nP	6.60	5.11	6.32	5.28	4.28	5.45
C_7N	6.97	6.44	7.12	1.12	1.15	1.18
C_7iP	6.90	6.09	6.56	10.67	9.90	10.08
C_7nP	6.48	5.59	6.81	3.95	3.56	4.54
C_8N	6.69	7.03	7.51	1.17	0.72	0.67
C_8iP	7.29	7.02	7.21	6.85	7.95	8.18
C_8nP	5.68	5.18	5.82	2.02	1.97	2.33
$C_9 + N$	7.41	12.45	9.25	1.77	0.52	0.29
C_9iP	6.59	6.38	6.10	3.90	4.90	4.47
C_9nP	4.42	4.26	4.70	0.87	.90	0.96
$C_{10} + iP$	4.29	7.34	5.20	3.51	2.66	1.58
$C_{10} + nP$	3.37	3.65	2.91	0.89	1.20	0.23

Analysis of Sulfur Compounds in Naphtha

The detection and subsequent removal of sulfur-containing compounds from petroleum feedstocks is very important in petroleum refining. Because sulfur compounds are responsible for poisoning the catalytic process, their detection and quantitation in feedstocks is vital. Selective detection of trace quantities of sulfur compounds in a complex hydrocarbon matrix, such as petroleum naphtha, can be achieved using a gas chromatograph equipped with a flame photometric detector. Separation can be optimized with a high resolution capillary column designed specifically for the separation of petroleum naphtha samples, as previously described. The experimental conditions are listed in Table 8-6.

Table 8-6.   **Conditions for the Analysis of Sulfur in Petroleum Feedstocks.**

HEATED ZONES		
ZONE	**DESCRIPTION**	**SET POINT °C**
1	Prefractionator Inlet	340
2	Transfer Line	200
3	Capillary Inlet	340
4	Valve Compartment	290
5	FID	350
6	FPD	280

Analytical column:	50 m x 0.2 mm x 0.5 μm
Stationary phase:	Cross-linked dimethylsilicone
Prefractionator columns:	2 ft x 1/8 inch 5% OV-101
	1 ft x 1/8 inch mol sieve 5A
Carrier gas:	$\bar{\mu}$ = 20 cm/sec, Helium
Split ratio:	400:1
Sample introduction:	1 μl or 2 μl manual injection
Oven temperature profile:	
Initial Value:	50°C
Initial Time:	0.5 min
Level 1:	18°C/min to 170°C
Level 2:	3°C/min to 300°C
Final Time:	2 min
Detectors:	
Flame Photometric:	
Filter:	Sulfur, 393 nm
Air:	100 ml/min
Hydrogen:	75 ml/min
Flame Ionization:	
Air:	400 ml/min
Hydrogen:	30 ml/min
Capillary makeup:	Nitrogen, 30 ml/min

For the determination of thiophenic sulfur in heavy fractions of petroleum feedstocks and crude oils, a specially modified GC with a prefractionator inlet interfaced to a standard split capillary inlet can be used (10). The valve configuration for the prefractionator used in this analysis is shown in Figure 8-8. The sample is injected through the prefractionator inlet onto a short OV-101 precolumn which separates the components according to their boiling points. To protect the high resolution capillary column, valve timing is set so that the $C_{20}+$ heavy fractions are backflushed to vent. The lighter fraction of the sample is transferred to the analytical column for further separation and identification. A typical chromatogram for the hydrotreater feedstock containing 1.5 weight percent sulfur is shown in Figure 8-9. The use of a high-efficiency column minimizes the coelution of high concentrations of hydrocarbons and sulfur-containing compounds which could cause FPD signal quenching. The flame photometric detector demonstrates excellent sensitivity and selectivity for this application as compared with the FID chromatogram in Figure 8-10. Sulfur quantitation is done by multilevel calibration because of the nonlinear response of the FPD to sulfur. Calibration curves for selected thiophenes are given in Figure 8-11.

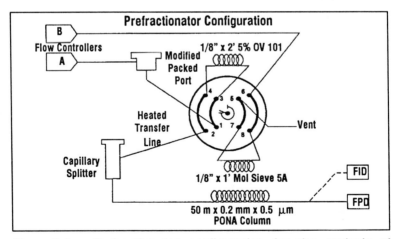

Figure 8-8. Prefractionator configuration for the analysis of sulfur in petroleum feedstocks.

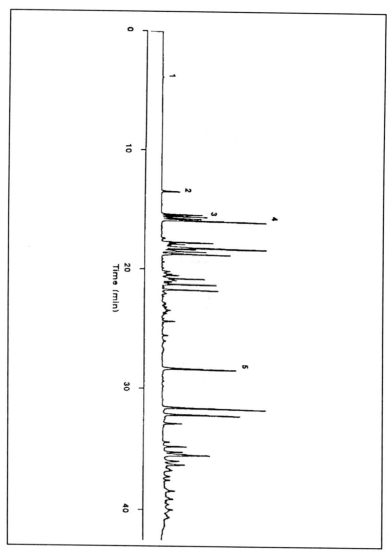

Figure 8-9.   FPD chromatogram of a gas-oil hydrotreater feed,
total sulfur is 1.5% wt. 1) methyl mercaptan;
2) benzothiophene; 3) methyl-substituted benzo-
thiophenes; 4) 3-methyl benzo[b]thiophene; 5) di-
benzothiophene. 1 μl injection, attn 2^4.

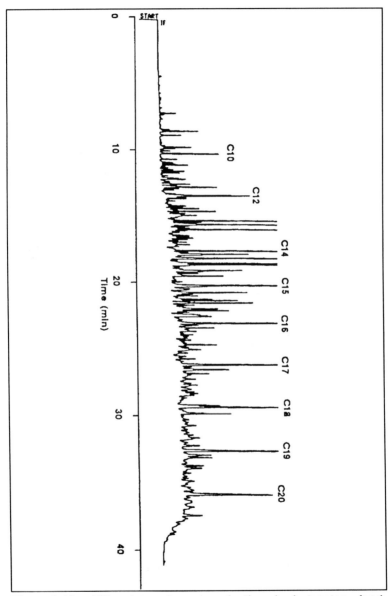

Figure 8-10.   FID   chromatogram   of   the   hydrotreater   feed.
Normal hydrocarbons are identified. 2 μl injection,
attn 2^6.

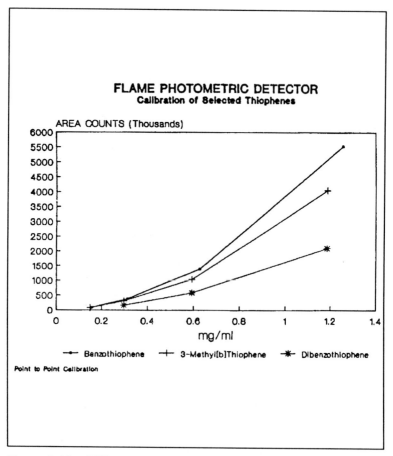

Figure 8-11. FPD response to selected thiophenes.

Determination of Oxygenates in Gasoline

The current international emphasis on the removal of leaded compounds from automotive gasolines has spurred the use of other compounds, such as C_1–C_4 alcohols and methyl tertiary butylether (MTBE), to improve octane ratings. This has produced an urgent need for a simple and rapid method to determine oxygenated compounds in gasoline. Multi-dimensional GC analysis has been described for gasoline/alcohol blends using a large bore FSWCOT column (11).

The valve diagram of a multidimensional GC system is shown in Figure 8-12. The lower efficiency and ability to apply a thick stationary phase film make the large diameter column suitable for the separation of low molecular weight oxygenated compounds.

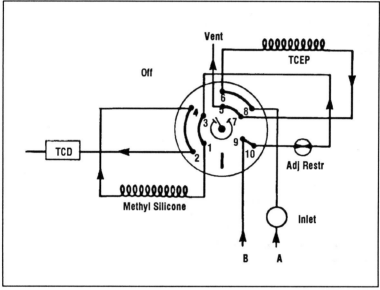

Figure 8-12. Valve diagram of capillary MD-GC system for gasoline/ alcohol blend analysis.

The two columns used are a large diameter WCOT column (30 m x 0.53 mm) coated with cross-linked methylsilicone and a micropacked precolumn packed with 20% TCEP coated on Chromosorb PAW 80/100 mesh. The analytical column is mounted in the oven and connected to the valve using zero dead volume connectors and stainless steel tubing. A low-flow needle valve is used to obtain the same flow to the TCD for both positions of the valve.

Sample is injected into the precolumn, as shown in Figure 8-12. Lighter hydrocarbons ($<C_6$) are vented out of the precolumn. Before methyl tertiary-butylether (MTBE) is eluted from the precolumn, the valve is switched to the "ON" position. The remainder of the sample is backflushed into the analytical column, and all C_1–C_4 alcohols, MTBE, and benzene are separated on the analytical column. Then the valve is returned to "OFF" position as soon as benzene is eluted, reversing flow in the capillary column; and the heavier hydrocarbons are backflushed as one peak to the TCD.

Figure 8-13 compares a typical chromatogram obtained with a blend of oxygenates in a gasoline sample to a chromatogram of gasoline without oxygenates. All C_1–C_4 alcohols and MTBE are separated with a total analysis time of 15 minutes. No interference from the gasoline matrix is observed as shown in Figure 8-14 for the analysis of a gasoline sample without backflushing.

An internal standard method (ISTD) is used for quantitation, with tertiary-amyl-alcohol (peak 10 in Figure 8-13) as the internal standard. Table 8-7 tabulates the results for repetitive runs of a blend of oxygenates in gasoline obtained using this method. Both precision and accuracy for this analysis are quite satisfactory.

For routine control analyses, an external standard method (ESTD) would probably be more desirable than the ISTD because no weighing of the sample is required. A comparison of the two methods, ISTD and ESTD, is shown in Table 8-8 for five different oxygenated gasolines.

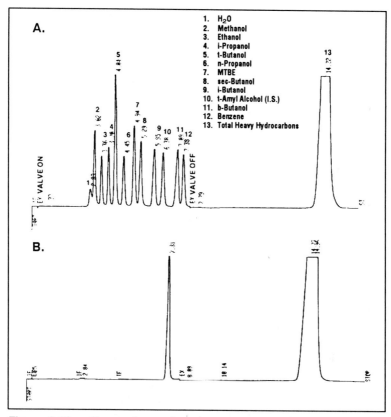

Figure 8-13. Comparison of a chromatogram of (A) a gasoline/ oxygenate blend and (B) gasoline without oxygenates. Columns and valve temperature: 60°C. Injection port temperature: 200°C. TCD temperature: 200°C.

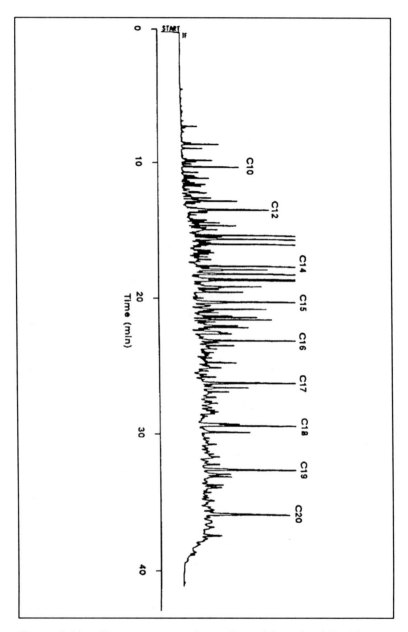

Figure 8-14.   Chromatogram of gasoline without backflushing.

Table 8-7.   Analysis of Oxygenates Blend.

Analysis of Oxygenates Blend

	BLEND	VOL% (a)							VOL% (b)	
		1	2	3	4	5	AVG	δ	1	2
Methanol	2.28	2.35	2.30	2.34	2.35	2.30	2.33	0.026	2.38	2.37
Ethanol	2.34	2.41	2.36	2.41	2.40	2.37	2.39	0.023	2.41	2.40
i-Propanol	1.42	1.51	1.48	1.52	1.51	1.49	1.50	0.016	1.50	1.52
n-Propanol	2.61	2.78	2.75	2.79	2.77	2.76	2.77	0.016	2.69	2.71
MTBE	2.74	2.76	2.74	2.77	2.76	2.76	2.76	0.012	2.78	2.81
i-Butanol	1.37	1.43	1.41	1.43	1.42	1.41	1.42	0.010	1.40	1.41
Sec-Butanol	2.41	2.47	2.46	2.47	2.46	2.46	2.46	0.005	2.41	2.41
i-Butanol	1.73	1.75	1.75	1.75	1.75	1.75	1.75	0	1.73	1.73
n-Butanol	4.62	4.80	4.83	4.80	4.81	4.82	4.81	.013	4.81	4.81

a) ISTD Method, 0.16 μl sample

b) Analyzed after four-month interval

Table 8-8.   Comparison of Quantitation Results for the MD-GC Analysis
of Gasolines.

Analysis of Gasolines

	1		2		3		4		5	
	ESTD	ISTD	ESTD	ISTD	ESTD	ISTD	ESTD	ISTD	ESTD	ISTD
Methanol	3.20	3.50	—	—	—	—	1.53	1.62	—	—
Ethanol	—	—	7.51	7.58	0.16	0.18	0.08	0.08	0.89	0.89
i-Propanol	2.94	2.91	—	—	5.67	5.70	—	—	0.29	0.29
n-Propanol	—	—	0.11	0.12	0.95	0.96	—	—	1.95	1.95
MTBE	3.66	3.75	—	—	0.18	0.18	1.91	1.88	—	—
t-Butanol	0.26	0.22	1.91	1.95	—	—	3.90	3.89	—	—
Sec-Butanol	—	—	0.99	1.02	—	—	0.13	0.15	0.48	0.50
i-Butanol	2.03	2.05	—	—	0.30	0.29	—	—	5.82	6.00
n-Butanol	0.23	0.19	2.01	2.00	—	—	4.30	4.23	—	—

Analysis of Natural Gas

The increase in the price of natural gas has prompted increased interest in a GC method that provides a more detailed analysis of the C_6+ portion of the gas. A schematic diagram of a newly designed system for natural gas analysis, employing two valves and a single-filament TCD, is shown in Figure 8-15 (12). The precolumn is a micropacked column, 1.6 mm od x 0.78 mm id x 1 m, packed with 10% OV-101 on 80/100 mesh Chromosorb P. Three analytical columns are used for this analysis. The WCOT column is a 30 m x 0.53 mm cross-linked methylsilicone column. MPC-3 is a micropacked column, 0.8 m long, packed with Porapak N, 80/100 mesh. MPC-4 is another micropacked column, 1 m long, packed with molecular sieve 13X, 60/80 mesh. The WCOT column is mounted in the oven, and the remaining two columns are connected directly to the valves in the valve oven.

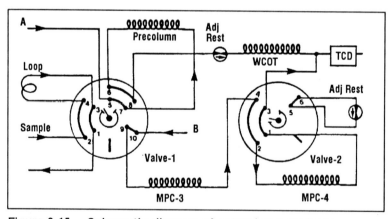

Figure 8-15. Schematic diagram of natural gas analysis.

The gas sample is injected into the precolumn when Valve-1 is switched "ON." The light portion of the sample ($<C_3$) is eluted from the precolumn into MPC-3 (Porapak N) and MPC-4 (molecular sieve 13X) in series. Just before CO_2 is eluted from (MPC-3), Valve-2 is switched "ON" to isolate MPC-4. This causes O_2, N_2, and CH_4 to be trapped in this column while CO_2

and C_2H_6 are eluted from MPC-3 and measured by the TCD. When C_2H_6 has been detected, Valve-2 is returned to "OFF" and O_2, N_2, CH_4 are separated and recorded. While these separations are in progress, the heavier portion of the sample ($>C_2$) in the precolumn is backflushed into the WCOT column and separated into the C_3–C_8 components. Figure 8-16 shows a chromatogram of a natural gas sample obtained using this system. All permanent gases and C_1–C_8 hydrocarbons are separated in 10 minutes. Because of the larger capacity of the columns and splitless sampling, the minimum detection of individual heavier components can be as low as 50 ppm with the microvolume TCD.

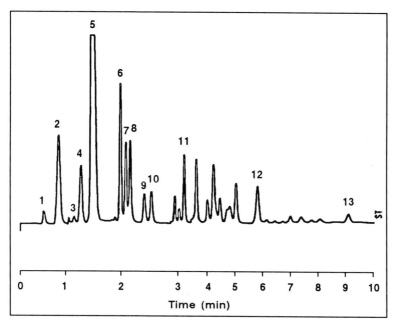

Figure 8-16. Chromatogram of natural gas sample. Column and valve temperature: 70°C; Carrier gas: hydrogen 4.3 ml/min, Sample size 20 µl (1) CO_2, (2) ethane, (3) O_2, (4) N_2, (5) methane, (6) propane, (7) i-butane, (8) n-butane, (9) i-pentane, (10) n-pentane, (11) n-hexane, (12) n-heptane, (13) n-octane.

Analysis of Refinery Gas

By substituting a 50 m Al$_2$O$_3$ PLOT column for the WCOT column in the system shown in Figure 8-15, all components through n-C$_5$ (except H$_2$) can be separated in only 4 minutes. A typical chromatogram is shown in Figure 8-17.

A second TCD may be added to the GC to measure H$_2$ from a separate injection of sample using nitrogen as the carrier gas. The capacity of the Al$_2$O$_3$ PLOT column is much smaller than that of the methylsilicone large bore column used in the analysis of natural gas. Injection volume is limited to approximately 5 µl. Splitting the flow before the PLOT column could solve the problem, but a better solution is to use a large bore Al$_2$O$_3$ PLOT column with higher sample capacity.

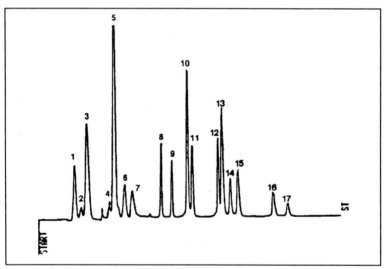

Figure 8-17. Chromatogram of refinery gas sample. Precolumn temperature: 76°C, Al$_2$O$_3$ PLOT columns temperature (oven) 120°C. Carrier gas: hydrogen 4.3 ml/min, Sample size: 4 ml. (1) CO$_2$, (2) ethylene, (3) ethane, (4) O$_2$, (5) N$_2$, (6) methane, (7) CO, (8) propane, (9) propylene, (10) i-butane, (11) n-butane, (12) t-butene-2, (13) butene-1, (14) i-butene, (15) c-butene-2, (16) i-pentane, (17) n-pentane.

Applications in the Life Sciences

In the life sciences, gas chromatography is widely used for the analyses of various chemical substances. Although HPLC is rapidly growing in this industry, capillary gas chromatography has maintained popularity in areas where plasma and urinary detection levels for chemical substances are below the threshold of the UV and fluorescent detectors.

When using gas chromatography for clinical analysis, sample matrices and injection techniques require special consideration. Alterations in the normal separation characteristics of a column can occur with repeated exposure to water and the deposition of nonvolatile components. Therefore, methods of sample introduction other than liquid injection should be considered when applicable. One example is the determination of alcohol levels in blood by headspace sampling techniques.

To minimize matrix interference, selective detectors are commonly used for biological samples. In most cases, these detectors are more sensitive for specific elements than the thermal conductivity (TCD) and the flame ionization (FID) detectors, making them ideal for trace analyses in complex matrices. The number of extraction and concentration steps can, therefore, be significantly reduced or even eliminated. Some of the more commonly used selective detectors in gas chromatography are: the electron capture (ECD) for chlorinated compounds; flame photometric (FPD) for sulfur- and phosphorus-containing molecules; and nitrogen-phosphorus (NPD) for the phosphorus and nitrogen compounds. Also, with the recent development of hyphenated gas chromatographic techniques, such as GC-MS and GC-IR, the clinical analyst now has a complete portfolio of GC detection devices for the structural elucidation of a chemical substance.

Analysis of Drugs of Abuse

The analysis of drugs of abuse in body fluids is usually performed in a sequence of two or more steps. A positive result can have potentially serious consequences; therefore, it is important that the confirmatory technique be definitive.

The standard confirmatory technique for drug testing is GC-MS (gas chromatography-mass spectroscopy). Capillary GC is widely used for prescreening. Although RIA (radioimmuno-assay) is faster and more economical, it is approximately 35% reliable and only specific for particular drugs. Because of its reproducibility, sensitivity, and more general utility, capillary GC is a preferred screening method for many laboratories.

Should the screening method selected give a positive result, the sample is then analyzed by GC-MS to confirm the presence of the drug. Figure 8-18 shows the total ion chromatogram (TIC) of a drug standard mixture. Table 8-9 gives the specific ions which, when detected within the specified retention time window, indicate the presence of a drug in a sample. Confirmation is achieved in one of two ways. With the scanning method, the mass spectrum is acquired and compared to that of a known standard or MS library as shown in Figure 8-19. For higher sensitivity, a selected ion method is applied. Here only the ions of interest are detected and the ratios of ion intensities are measured and compared to deuterated internal standards.

Using capillary GC, drug substances can be identified by measuring their retention times or retention indices and comparing the measured values to those of drug standards. A practical application of this technique is seen in the dual-column capillary analysis for drugs of abuse. The method is based upon determining the retention properties of chemical substances separated on two capillary columns coated with different stationary phases (13-14).

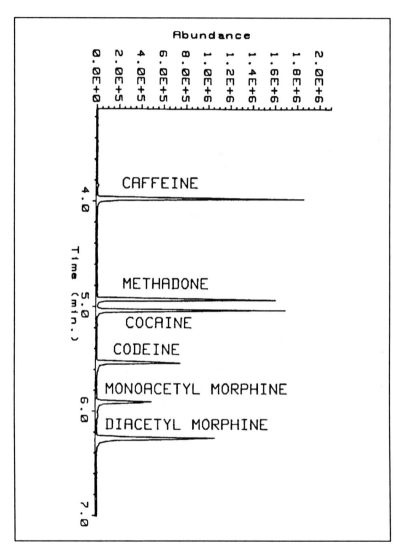

Figure 8-18.   TIC of drug standard mixture.

Table 8-9.   Primary and Confirming Ions for the Drug Standard
Mixture shown in Figure 8-18.

COMPOUND NAME	t_R	Primary Ion	Confirming Ion No. 1	Confirming Ion No. 2
caffeine (ISTD)	3.98	194	109	67
methadone	4.94	72	294	--
cocaine	5.04	303	82	182
codeine	5.54	299	162	229
monoacetyl morphine	5.92	327	268	215
heroin	6.27	369	327	310

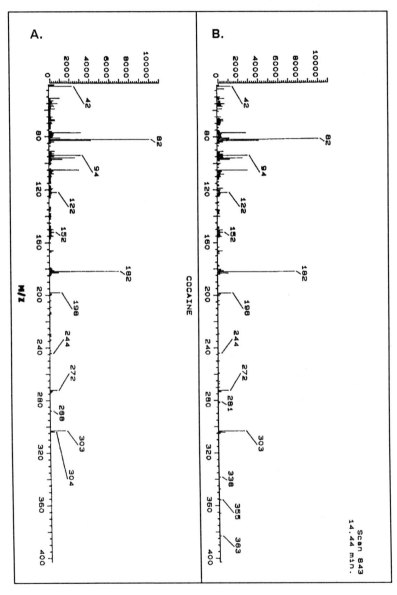

Figure 8-19. Comparison of A. Reference mass spectrum of cocaine, with B. Mass spectrum of unknown sample. (From HP Application Note GCMS87-1)

In an application described by Hyver (15), a minicomputer-based, dedicated GC workstation is configured to a GC equipped with a capillary split/splitless inlet and dual FID. The two capillary columns are installed in a single injection port using a two-holed ferrule. The columns are matched with regard to their geometry and the operating range and retention behavior. The 5% and 50% phenylmethlysilicone capillary columns are installed into separate flame ionization detectors. The dual channel chromatograms for an alkaloid drug standard mixture and the calibration reference used for the retention index calculation are shown in Figure 8-20.

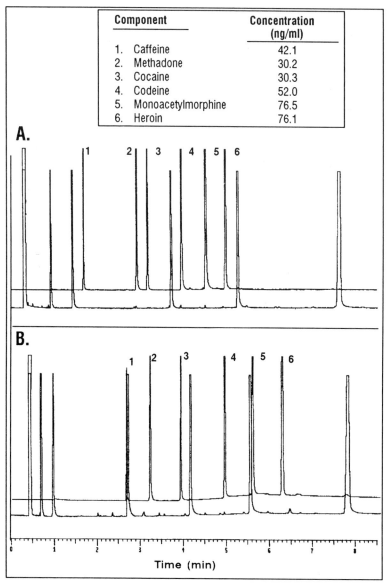

Component	Concentration (ng/ml)
1. Caffeine	42.1
2. Methadone	30.2
3. Cocaine	30.3
4. Codeine	52.0
5. Monoacetylmorphine	76.5
6. Heroin	76.1

Time (min)

Figure 8-20. Chromatograms for the alkaloid drug standard mixture compared to the hydrocarbon calibration mixture separated on (A) 5% phenylmethyl silicone, and (B) 50% phenylmethyl silicone.

Analysis of Tricyclic Antipsychotic Agents by Flame Photometric Detection (FPD)

The determination of tricyclic antipsychotic agents using capillary gas chromatography with flame photometric detection (FPD) is a very valuable technique for therapeutic drug monitoring. Following the discovery of the antipsychotic activity of chlorpromazine nearly forty years ago, various derivatives of this phenothiazine drug were synthesized and approved for use in humans. Some examples are listed in Table 8-10. The thiothixene family of tricyclics also shows good therapeutic activity as an antipsychotic. In addition to antipsychotic activities, some phenothiazine derivatives are also prescribed for the control of nausea and vomiting. These complex structured therapeutic agents were analyzed by gas chromatography using packed columns and FID. With packed column methods, it is difficult to separate and differentiate the various phenothiazine and thiothixene derivatives from their metabolites and other components in the physiological matrix.

Table 8-10.   Typical Tricyclic Antipsychotics.

A. Phenothiazine derivative   B. Thioxanthene derivative

Name	Derivative	X	R	Wt. % S
Promethazine	A	H	$CH_2CH(CH_3)N(CH_3)_2$	11.25
Promazine	A	H	$(CH_2)_3N(CH_3)_2$	11.25
Thioridazine	A	SCH_3	$(CH_2)_3$—(N-CH_3 piperidine)	17.27
Triflupromazine	A	CF_3	$(CH_2)_3N(CH_3)_2$	9.08
Ethopropazine	A	H	$CH_2CH(CH_3)N(C_2H_5)_2$	10.02
Mesoridazine	A	$SOCH_3$	$(CH_2)_2$—(N-CH_3 piperidine)	16.56
Chlorprothixene	B	Cl	$CH(CH_2)_2N(CH_3)_2$	10.13

The inertness of fused silica capillary columns makes analysis of the antipsychotics without derivatization possible. In addition, the capillary analysis gives improved resolution with a shorter analysis time compared with the packed column method. A sensitive and selective method for the determination of sulfur-containing tricyclic antipsychotic agents by capillary GC is described (16) using flame photometric detection. Five sulfur-containing tricyclics (triflupromazine, promethazine, promazine, chlorprothixene, and thioridazine) are separated using a fused silica WCOT column (12 m x 0.2 mm) coated with a 0.33 μm film of cross-linked 5% phenylmethyl silicone.

A typical chromatogram of this separation is shown in Figure 8-21 using a flame photometric detector. The minimum detectable level of the method was determined to be 0.2 ng/component, or approximately 20 pg sulfur. The FPD sulfur response is known to be nonlinear; therefore, quantitation is achieved using multilevel calibration methods. Nonlinear detector response curves for promazine and chlorprothixene are shown in Figure 8-22. The results of the statistical analysis of the response data are given in Table 8-11.

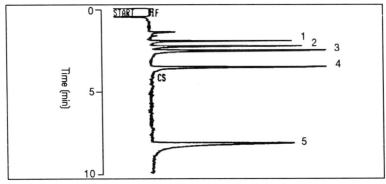

Figure 8-21.   FPD chromatogram of tricyclic antipsychotic agents 1. triflupromazine, 2. promethazine, 3. promazine, 4. chlorprothixene and 5. thioridazine at approximately 3 ng per component. Column: HP Ultra-2 12 m x 0.2 mm x 0.33 μm cross-linked 5% phenylmethyl silicone.

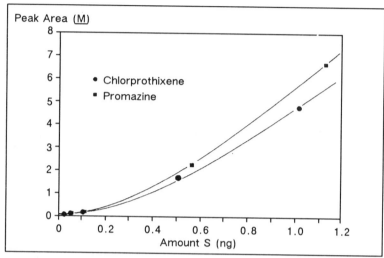

Figure 8-22. Flame photometric detector response for sulfur. Plot of peak area vs. amount sulfur for ■ promazine and ● chlorprothixene.

Table 8-11. Flame Photometric Detector Response Promazine and Chlorprothixene.

Amount per Component (ng)	PROMAZINE Amount Sulfur (ng)	PROMAZINE Mean * Peak Area	CHLORPROTHIXENE Amount Sulfur (ng)	CHLORPROTHIXENE Mean * Peak Area
0.2	0.023	14779 (0.072)**	0.020	11374 (0.252)
0.5	0.056	57709 (0.059)	0.051	52722 (0.056)
1.0	0.113	128198 (0.055)	0.101	112220 (0.056)
5.0	0.563	2203175 (0.014)	0.507	1622150 (0.017)
10.0	1.125	6613380 (0.017)	1.013	4720220 (0.026)

Regression results:

n		1.58		1.54
C		5.487×10^6		4.626×10^6
Correlation Coefficient		0.9997		0.9993

*   Mean of 5 observations
** Parenthetical values indicate the coefficient of variance.

Automated On-Column Methods for Antiepileptic Drugs (AED)

Gas chromatography has been used extensively for the therapeutic monitoring of antiepileptic drugs (AED). A few of the major drugs used for the treatment of various forms of epilepsy are carbamazepine, clonazepam, phenobarbital, valproic acid, phenytoin, ethosuximide, and primidone. Monitoring plasma levels of patients on therapeutic doses of these drugs is important due to the necessity of achieving and maintaining the narrow dosage ranges which will provide therapy to deter epileptic episodes without causing toxic side effects.

Two approaches exist in the therapeutic monitoring of antiepileptic drugs, namely chromatography and immunoassay. Gas chromatography is accepted as the international standard for the therapeutic monitoring of AED (17–19). Surprisingly, however, in the literature very few routine clinical methods recommend the use of capillary columns for this analysis. The two primary reasons given are the complexity of capillary instrumentation and the limited working range of sample capacity for capillary columns. These problems can be eliminated by using wide diameter (>0.53 mm id) columns. These columns offer a wide linear range in sample capacity, as well as ease of use and interface to packed column instruments.

Another advantage of the capillary method in comparison to packed methods is that a single column can separate all of the desired drugs within a shorter analysis time. More reliable qualitative and quantitative chromatographic information can be obtained using a fused silica open tubular system. FID is the most widely used detector for AED, but element-selective detectors such as the nitrogen-phosphorus detector (NPD) can increase sensitivity for the detection of trace level drugs containing nitrogen. On-column injection with wide diameter fused silica WCOT columns provides the advantages of gentle sample introduction with inertness for the analysis of the underived drugs.

Gabrio and Hyver (20) described the extraction of antiepileptic drugs from plasma and the subsequent analysis using on-column GC methods. The AEDs were analyzed as groups, since their therapeutic concentrations in plasma vary from as high as 100 µg/ml for valproic acid to as low as 0.003 µg/ml for the clonazepam as shown in Table 8-12. Plasma extraction techniques for the AEDs were optimized for these expected variations in the minimum concentration of the compounds in fluids. The separation of AEDs was achieved using 10 m 530 µ id columns, as shown in Figure 8-23. Chromatograms for the separation of the various groups of AEDs extracted from plasma are shown in Figure 8-24.

Table 8-12.   Therapeutic Range and Retention Indices for Common Antiepileptic Drugs.

Group	Drug	Therapeutic Range (µg/ml)	Kovats' Retention Index on OV-1
1	Valproic Acid	50–100	1108*
	Ethosuximide	40–100	1220
2	Phenobarbital	20–40	1960
	Primidone	8–12	2250
	Carbamazepine	6–10	2290
	Phenytoin	10–20	2330
3	Clonazepam	0.003–0.06	2860

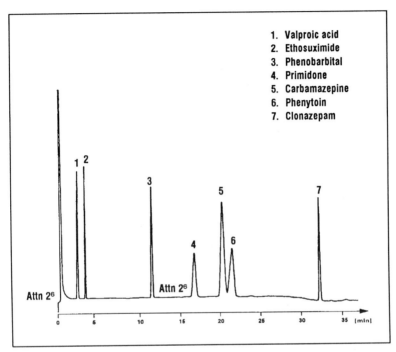

Figure 8-23. Separation of antiepileptic drug standards (0.1 mg/ml chloroform) using on-column injection. Column 10 m x 0.53 mm x 2.65 μm HP-1 Series 530 μ column. Gas chromatograph: HP 5880A. Carrier gas: nitrogen, 4 ml/min. Oven temperature profile: 100°C programmed to 200°C at 10°C/min with 16 min final hold. Detector: FID.

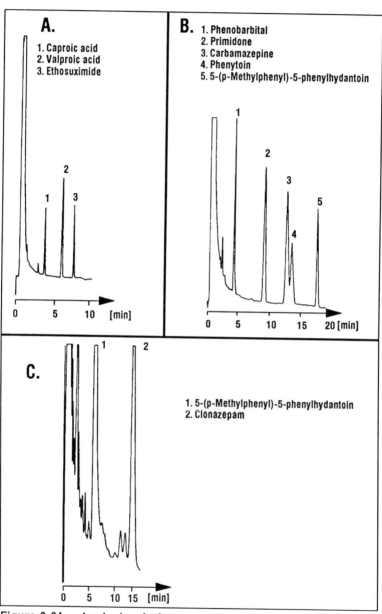

Figure 8-24. Analysis of plasma extracts containing AEDs from (A) Group I, (B) Group II, and (C) Group III in Table 8-12.

Blood Alcohol Analysis Using Headspace Sampling

Headspace sampling for the analysis of alcohol in urine, blood, and breath provides a convenient method of introducing volatile components from problematic biological matrices. Headspace sampling can be easily automated using BASIC programming of the autocalibration, statistical calculation, second column confirmation, and special case sample report formatting. A dual-channel GC uses two capillary columns mounted in one injection port with connection to two flame ionization detectors. The headspace injection uses a 10:1 split of the sample. Minimum detection limits for ethanol is 0.055% w/v. Separation is achieved at an isothermal temperature of 60°C or below. Typical chromatograms from this application are shown in Figure 8-25.

Metabolic Profiling

Capillary gas chromatography can be used effectively for the analysis of cellular fatty acid from bacteria (21). The analysis is performed by comparing the chromatographic profiles of bacterial fatty acids with reference profiles stored in a computer-generated library. The technique is applicable to all bacteria in pure culture. It is a time- and cost-effective solution compared to traditional microbial identification techniques. Chromatograms of the calibration standard and a known bacteria are shown in Figure 8-26. This approach can also be applied generically in other areas of metabolic profiling, such as in the analysis of steroids and organic acids in urine.

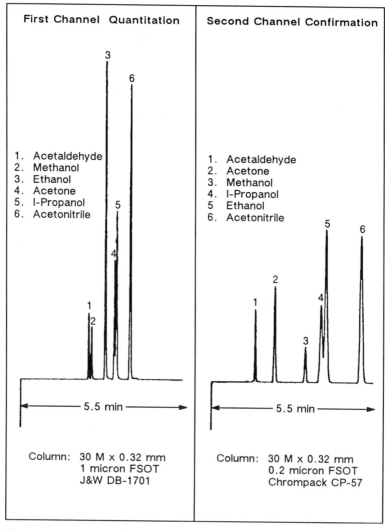

First Channel Quantitation

3

6

1. Acetaldehyde
2. Methanol
3. Ethanol
4. Acetone
5. I-Propanol
6. Acetonitrile

5

4

1

2

◀— 5.5 min —▶

Column: 30 M x 0.32 mm
1 micron FSOT
J&W DB-1701

Second Channel Confirmation

1. Acetaldehyde
2. Acetone
3. Methanol
4. I-Propanol
5 Ethanol
6. Acetonitrile

5

6

2

1

4

3

◀— 5.5 min —▶

Column: 30 M x 0.32 mm
0.2 micron FSOT
Chrompack CP-57

Figure 8-25. A dual-channel analysis of blood alcohol using headspace sampling.

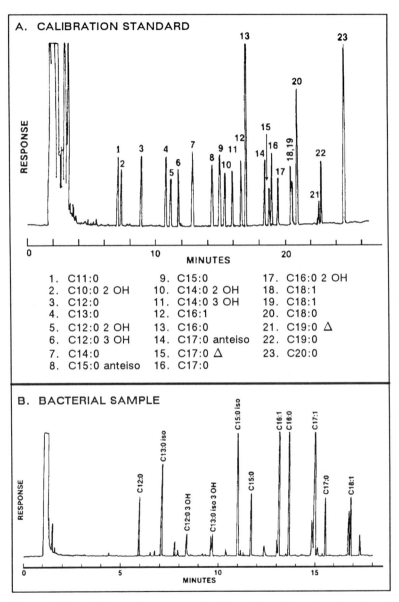

Figure 8-26. Chromatograms of (A) calibration standard and
(b) known bacterial sample of Alteromonas
putrefaciens.

Applications in Foods, Flavors, and Commodities

Separation, detection, characterization, and monitoring of chemical substances is very important to the manufacturing and regulation of the foods and flavors industry. Capillary gas chromatography is used extensively in almost every segment of this industry.

Due to potential human toxicity, in 1986 the FDA banned the use of sulfiting agents as preservatives on fresh fruits and vegetables in the U.S. The Monier Williams method, a very time-consuming and laborious wet chemistry method, has been the industry standard for measuring sulfur compounds in food. Recently Merrick-Gass et al. (22) developed a quick, reliable, and accurate method for sulfite determination in foods using headspace capillary gas chromatography. Using an FPD operating in the sulfur mode, the presence of sulfiting agents in fresh shrimp and lettuce was detected at the parts-per-million level, as evidenced by the chromatograms in Figure 8-27.

The use of gas chromatography with selective detection for determining pesticide residues in food is well documented. Organophosphorus compounds are detected reliably with the FPD operating in the phosphorus mode. Sample extracts of fresh produce are analyzed by direct injection techniques. Chromatograms for the analysis of pesticides in celery and lettuce samples are shown in Figure 8-28.

Dual-column capillary methods are commonly used in the food and flavor industry. For the characterization of essential oils, the chromatographic fingerprints and/or retention indices are compared on two columns with different stationary phase polarities as shown for the analysis of lime oil in Figure 8-29. The hardware configuration for this analysis described by Phillips et al. (23) is shown in Figure 8-30. The flexibility and ruggedness of fused silica capillary columns allows the installation of both columns into a common injection port. The analysis requires synchronous data acquisition and post-run retention index calculation. The retention indices for selected

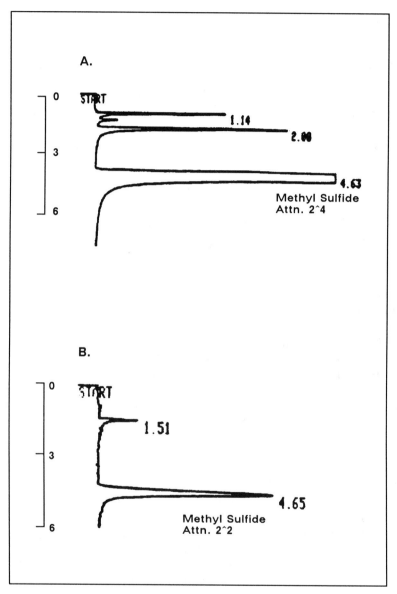

Figure 8-27. Analysis of sulfiting agents in A. Fresh frozen shrimp, and B. Fresh lettuce by headspace sampling and flame photometric detection.

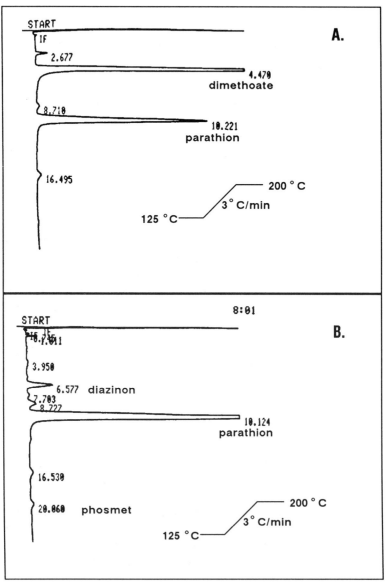

Figure 8-28. Chromatograms of the analysis of organo-phosphorus pesticides in extracts of fresh produce. A. Lettuce and B. Celery (Courtesy of H.E. Brown, Ministry of Agriculture & Food, Ottawa, Canada).

components commonly found in naturally occurring essential oils are given in Table 8-13. Phillips and Wolstromer used this system to create an anthology of essential oil chromatograms (24).

Wylie (25) also used a dual column configuration with headspace sampling for fragrance and flavor analysis of consumer products. The use of headspace sampling not only minimized sample preparation, but also increased the applicability of the technique to a wider range of sample matrices such as shampoo and toothpaste.

Environmental Analysis

Within the past two decades, the concern over air and water pollution has prompted more stringent guidelines for the protection of the environment. Many methods call for the use of GC and GC-MS systems for the detection of chemical pollutants in a wide variety of environmental matrices. Environmental analysis has benefited from the recent advances in gas chromatography to include high resolution columns for complex mixtures, high sample capacity of large bore WCOT columns for volatiles, and improved sensitivity and selectivity in detection.

Analysis of Volatile Priority Pollutants

The U.S. Environmental Protection Agency (EPA) Method 601/602 specifies the analysis of volatile priority pollutants in wastewater. The EPA Method 601 is a gas chromatographic method for the analysis of 29 volatile halocarbons, and Method 602 is for the analysis of seven volatile aromatics. Purge and trap is the technique specified for the concentration and introduction of the volatile components into the gas chromatograph. The electrolytic conductivity (ELCD) and photoionization (PID) detectors are specified because of their respective selectivity for halocarbons and unsaturated compounds. For the analysis of drinking and raw source waters, the associated EPA Methods 502.1 and 503.1 require identical hardware.

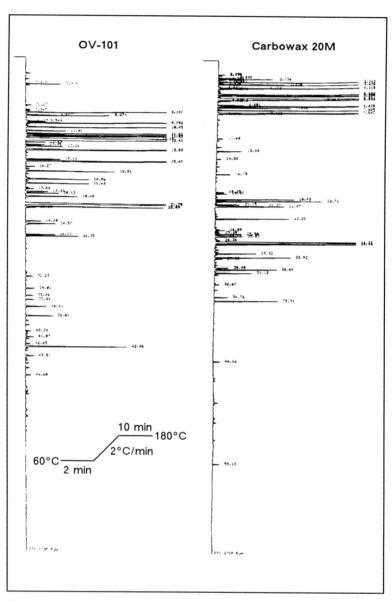

Figure 8-29. Lime oil distilled, Mexican. Columns: 50 m x 0.20 mm. Carrier gas: H_2, $\bar{\mu}$ = 40 cm/sec. Sample: 0.1 μl, split ratio 200:1.

Table 8-13.   Retention   Indices   of   Selected   Compounds
Commonly Found in Essential Oils.

Compound	Stationary phase Carbowax 20M	OV-101	Δ
α-thujene	394.3	533.8	+0140
α-pinene	387.1	540.2	+0153
camphene	427.6	552.6	+0125
sabinene	483.4	577.8	+0094
β-pinene	467.2	581.5	+0114
myrcene	526.0	599.3	+0073
α-phellandrene	511.7	616.9	+0105
α-terpinene	538.7	621.4	+0083
p-cymene	625.6	624.9	−0001
1,8-cineole	562.4	630.9	+0068
β-phellandrene	565.7	631.4	+0066
limonene	556.5	633.5	+0077
γ-terpinene	606.4	661.4	+0055
terpinolene	637.8	692.5	+0055
nonanal	748.3	700.6	−0048
linalool	904.7	707.5	−0197
terpinen-4-ol	940.2	776.6	−0164
α-terpineol	1031.8	792.3	−0240
neral	1011.5	832.8	−0179
nerol	1139.3	838.2	−0301
linalyl acetate	919.0	856.9	−0062
geranial	1187.2	865.7	−0322
geraniol	1187.8	865.7	−0322
safrole	1192.7	884.0	−0309
terpinyl acetate	1033.9	948.7	−0085
neryl acetate	1074.9	963.7	−0111
geranyl acetate	1105.1	982.1	−0123
b-caryophyllene	934.0	1023.3	−0089
α-humykene	1000.2	1056.3	+0056
elemicin	1470.3	1068.3	−0402
bisabolene	1072.1	1114.8	+0043
myristicin	1560.3	1116.3	−0444
eugenyl acetate	1565.0	1119.8	−0445

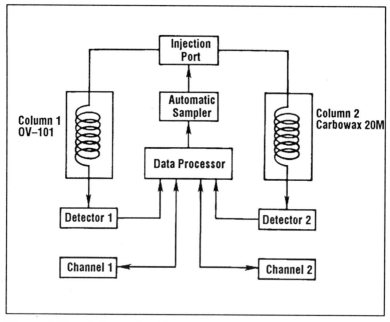

Figure 8-30. Schematic of hardware components of dual channel analysis.

Both the 500 and 600 series methods for water analyses are packed-column methods. Using the columns specified, a complete Method 601 analysis takes approximately 45–50 minutes, while all the Method 602 compounds elute within 20–25 minutes. Capillary columns are being used more frequently for these methods due to the drawbacks associated with packed columns (26). They include longer analysis time, poor resolution for the separation of all halocarbons, activity, and high column bleed. The fused silica capillary columns offer greater efficiency, inertness, and durability than packed columns for this application. However, the SP-1000 packed column does offer the advantage of resolving most volatile compounds without the need for cryogenic cooling. Capillary columns coated with tailor-made phases are commercially available and are the most popular choice of column for this analysis.

Wide bore capillary columns (0.53 mm id and greater) have distinct advantages over conventional narrow bore columns in purge and trap analysis. These columns can accept the high flow rate required during the trap desorption step; whereas, the smaller diameter capillary columns require cryogenic focusing. There are other compromises necessary for the smaller diameter capillary column methodology. Connecting the purge and trap transfer line to the packed column inlet (the recommended configuration for standard 601/602) causes an increase in dead volume. This slightly degrades resolution of the light components but permits syringe injection of known and standard samples. Direct connection of the purge and trap transfer line to the wide bore capillary column results in the best chromatographic performance, but prevents syringe injection.

Capillary analysis of volatile priority pollutants can be performed with a variety of columns and hardware configurations. Wylie (27) describes some of the possible configurations with references for further reading. The detectors for EPA Methods 601 and 602 can be connected in series since the PID is a nondestructive detector. The effluent can be directed to the ELCD for subsequent halogen analysis. To operate these detectors in series, a nonstandard hardware connection must be made. Typical chromatograms generated from a purge and trap analysis are shown in Figure 8-31, where PID and ELCD are connected in series. By replacing the specified packed columns with a 30 m x 0.53 mm DB-624 fused silica WCOT, baseline separation of most components is achieved with analysis time significantly reduced.

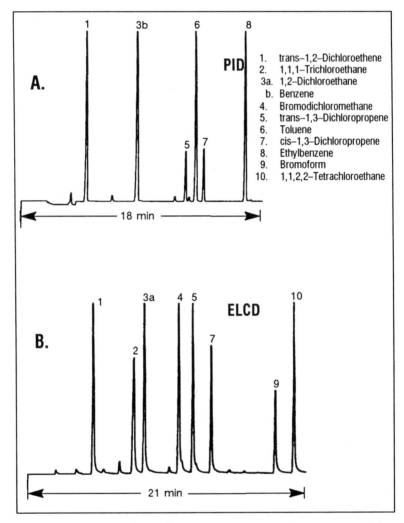

1. trans–1,2–Dichloroethene
2. 1,1,1–Trichloroethane
3a. 1,2–Dichloroethane
 b. Benzene
4. Bromodichloromethane
5. trans–1,3–Dichloropropene
6. Toluene
7. cis–1,3–Dichloropropene
8. Ethylbenzene
9. Bromoform
10. 1,1,2,2–Tetrachloroethane

Figure 8-31. Purge and trap injection of a sample containing volatile priority pollutants from both EPA Methods 601 and 602 (40 µg/l each) using a 0.53 mm id DB-624 fused silica capillary column coupled directly to the purge and trap transfer line. The ELCD was coupled in series with the PID.

For EPA Methods 601/602, headspace sampling can provide improved precision and comparable sensitivity to purge and trap (27, 28). In addition, headspace sampling offers advantages in applications for soil and sludge, as well as water samples. With headspace sampling, system contamination from samples that foam or have high levels of an analyte can be minimized. Comparison of the headspace results in Figure 8-32 to those of purge and trap in Figure 8-31 shows similar results except that the headspace sampling includes the four early eluting gases—chloromethane, vinyl chloride, bromomethane, and chloroethane. These peaks are missing in purge and trap because the gases are not retained by the recommended Tenax trap.

EPA Method 624 is a capillary GC-MS method for the analysis of volatile organic priority pollutant extracts from soil and sludge. A typical chromatogram is found in Figure 8-33. Identification of certain priority pollutants by mass spectroscopy is complicated by its limited ability to distinguish isomers, such as in the identification of di- and tri-substituted benzene compounds. Complementary spectroscopic techniques have joined the repertoire of detectors now available in gas chromatography. In addition to Fourier transform IRD, discussed in Chapter 5, specific elemental detection is now possible with atomic emission detection (AED).

The microwave-induced helium plasma (MIP), atomic emission detector (AED) has been used for GC analysis of pesticides. In principle, specific detection can be accomplished for any element in the periodic table that can be analyzed using GC. Detection limits for C, H, D, N, O, Br, Cl, F, S, Si, P, and Hg range from 0.1 to 75 pg/sec with selectivities of 19,000 or more. The GC-MIP-AED system can be used for the detection and elemental characterization of 27 different pesticides by obtaining element-specific chromatograms of C, H, N, O, Br, Cl, F, P, and S. By performing quantitative analysis for each element, it is possible to calculate the approximate empirical formula for 20 different herbicides in two different mixtures.

GC detectors currently used for EPA pesticide methods are selective for the detection of halogens, S, N, and P. However, the ECD and ELCD cannot differentiate between F, Cl, and Br. The FPD may suffer from quenching and has a nonlinear response. Because pesticides are rich in heteroatoms, they are particularly good candidates for GC-MIP-AED analysis. With GC-MIP-AED, complete elemental profiles can be obtained and/or individual elements in molecules can be detected. Figures 8-34 and 8-35 show element-specific chromatograms for diazinon and arochlor, respectively. The chromatograms for C, S, and N are obtained simultaneously using oxygen and hydrogen scavenger gases.

Powerful specific detection tools, coupled with the many technological advances in column, software, and hardware development over the past decade, have added a new dimension to GC. Since the introduction of the fused silica column, capillary chromatography capability for extended and specific analyses has burgeoned. Capillary columns permit the ready separation and specific analysis of many complex components which were difficult to analyze using packed column methods. In many segments of industry, such as forensic and therapeutic drug testing and environmental monitoring, capillary column GC-MS has become the standard confirmatory technique. Capillary GC has been applied to a variety of analytical problems because of its reliability in quantitative and qualitative information, repeatability of testing methodology, and shortened analysis time. As capillary column and associated technologies continue to evolve, and industrial analytical needs develop apace, more and more capillary column GC applications are developed. This continued steady growth of capillary GC gives a very good sign of continuing and evolving to the turn of the century.

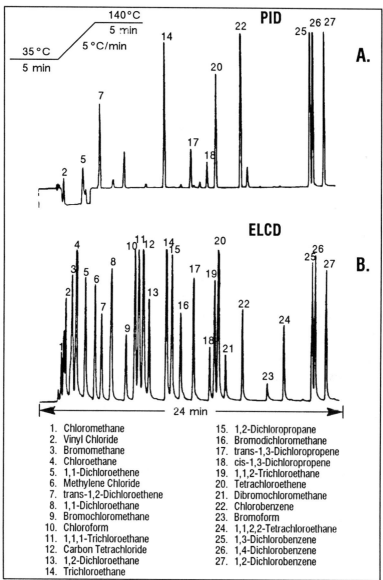

Figure 8-32. Headspace injection of a sample containing EPA Method 601 halocarbons at 20 µg/l each. The headspace transfer line was coupled directly to the 0.53 mm DB-624 column (Column C, Table 1); the ELCD and PID were operated in series.

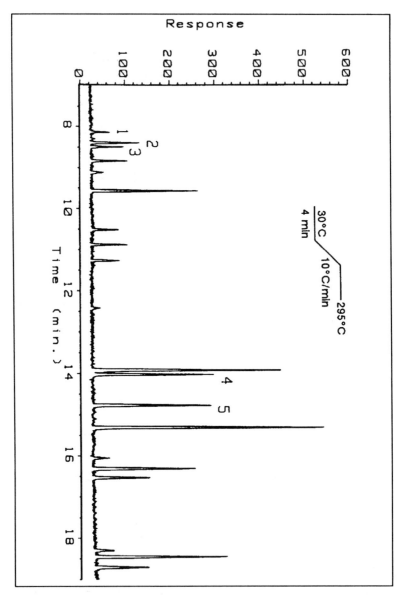

Figure 8-33. GC-MS chromatogram of a typical priority pollutant sample. Column: 12 m x 0.32 mm x 1.0 μ cross-linked 5% phenylmethyl silicone.

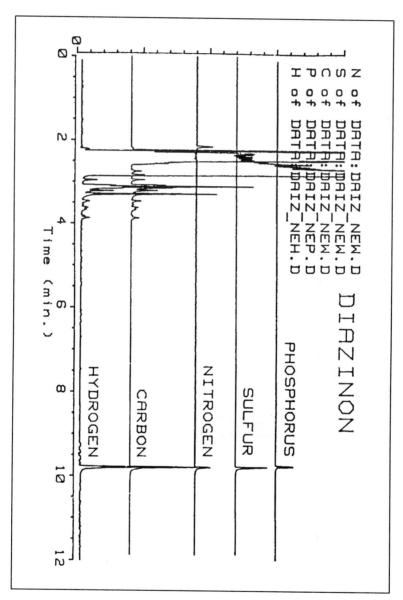

Figure 8-34. GC-MIP-AED analysis of diazinon. Oven temperature program: 100°C (1 min), 10°C/min to 250°C; inlet and transfer line temperatures = 200°C.

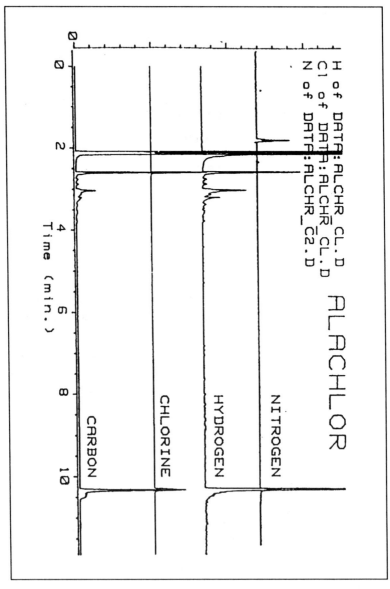

Figure 8-35.   GC-MIP-AED analysis of arochlor.   Oven temperature program: 100°C (1 min), 10°C/min to 250°C;
inlet and transfer line temperatures = 200°C.

References

1. ASTM Standard Method. *Simulated Distillation* D-2887, Part 24, (1978) 777.

2. Green, L. E. 1976. *Hydrocarbon Processing* pp 506.

3. Firor, R. L. January 1988. *Hewlett-Packard Application Note No. 228-60* Publication No. 43-5954-9198.

4. ASTM Standards, Part 23 (1974) 672.

5. ASTM Standards, Part 24 (1978) 724.

6. DiSanzo, F. P., and V. J. Giarrocco. 1988. *Proceedings of the Ninth International Symposium on Capillary Chromatography* pp 499–511. Heidelberg: Huethig Verlag.

7. Sadler, D. A. October 1980. *PONA Analysis by Gas Chromatography* Gulf Coast Instrumental Analysis Group, 69th Meeting.

8. Green, L. E., and E. Matt. September 1982. *Hewlett-Packard Technical Paper No. 100* Publication No. 43-5953-1656.

9. Naizhong, Zou, and L. E. Green. 1985. *Proceedings of the Sixth International Symposium on Capillary Chromatography* pp 466–475. Heidelberg: Huethig Verlag.

10. Firor, R. L. August 1987. *Hewlett-Packard Application Note No. 228-55* Publication No. 43-5954-9171.

11. Green, L. E. and Zou Naizhong. May 1986. *Hewlett-Packard Technical Paper No. 10* Publication No. 43-5953-1839.

12. Naizhong, Zou, and L. E. Green. February 1986. *Hewlett-Packard Technical Paper No. 116* Publication No. 43-5954-7566.

13. Watts, V. W., and T. F. Simonick. 1986. *J Anal Toxicol* 10:198–204.

14. Newton, B., and R. F. Foery. 1984. *J Anal Toxicol* 8:129–134.

15. Hyver, K. J. July 1987. *Hewlett-Packard Application Note No. 228-56* Publication No. 43-5954-9172.

16. Hyver, K. J. November 1986. *Hewlett-Packard Application Note No. 228-51* Publication No. 43-5954-7614.

17. Rambeck, B., and J. W. A. Meijer. 1980. *Ther Drug Monitor* 2:385–396.

18. Burke, J. T., and J. P. Thenot. 1985. *J Chromatogr* 340:199–241.

19. Meijer, J. W. A., B. Rambeck, and M. Riedmann. 1983. *Ther Drug Monitor* 5: 39–53.

20. Hyver, K. J., and Th. Gabrio. December 1987. *Hewlett-Packard Application Note No. 228-57* Publication No. 43-5954-9183.

21. Miller, L., and T. Berger. June 1985. *Hewlett-Packard Application Note No. 228-41* Publication No. 43-5953-1858.

22. Merrick-Gass, M. T., K. J. Hyver and D. DiUbaldo. December 1986. *Hewlett-Packard Application Note No. 228-53* Publication No. 43-5954-7620.

23. Phillips, R. J., R. J. Wolstromer, and R. R. Freeman. January 1981. *Hewlett-Packard Application Note No. 228-16* Publication No. 43-5953-1543.

24. Phillips, R. J., and R. J. Wolstromer. February 1981. *Hewlett-Packard Application Note No. 228-17* Publication No. 43-5953-1563.

25. Wylie, P. L. January 1986. *Hewlett-Packard Application Note No. 228-45* Publication No. 43-5954-7550.

26. Wylie, P. L. May 1987. *Hewlett-Packard Application Note No. 228-50* Publication No. 43-5954-7613.

27. Wylie, P. L. 1987. *Proceedings of the Eighth International Symposium on Capillary Chromatography*, pp 482–499. Heidelberg: Huethig Verlag.

28. Wylie, P. L. 1988. *J Amer Water Works Assoc* 80:65–72.

APPENDICES

APPENDIX I.   NOMENCLATURE

A	multiflow path term in the van Deemter Equation.
B	longitudinal diffusion term in the Golay Equation.
C	resistance to mass transfer in the Golay Equation.
$C_{i,m}$	concentration of component i in the mobile phase.
$C_{i,s}$	concentration of component i in the stationary phase.
C_m	resistance to mass transfer in the mobile phase.
C_s	resistance to mass transfer in the stationary phase.
D_m	diffusion coefficient in the mobile phase.
D_s	diffusion coefficient in the stationary phase.
d	column internal diameter.
d_f	stationary phase film thickness.
H	theoretical effective plate height equivalent.
h	theoretical plate height equivalent.
h_{min}	theoretical minimum value of h.
I_a^s	Kovats' retention index of component a measured on stationary phase s.
K_D	distribution coefficient.
k	partition ratio (capacity ratio).
L	column length.
N	number of effective theoretical plates.
n	number of theoretical plates.
$n_{i,m}$	number of moles of component i in the mobile phase.

$n_{i,s}$ number of moles of component i in the stationary phase.

R   resolution.

r   column internal radius.

TZ   Trennzahl or separation number.

t_m retention time of the unretained solute (column "holdup" or dead time).

t_R solute retention time.

t_R' adjusted retention time.

V_m column volume occupied by the mobile phase.

V_s column volume occupied by the stationary phase.

W_b peak width measured at the baseline.

W_h peak width at half height.

α relative retention time.

β phase ratio.

$\bar{\mu}$ average linear velocity of the mobile phase.

σ variance of chromatographic peak.

APPENDIX II. LIST OF ABBREVIATIONS

AED	atomic emission detector.
2D-GC	two-dimensional gas chromatography.
ECD	electron capture detector.
FID	flame ionization detector.
FPD	flame photometric detector.
FS	fused silica.
FSWCOT	fused silica wall coated open tubular column.
GC	gas chromatography.
GC-IR	gas chromatography/infrared detection.
GC-MS	gas chromatography/mass spectrometry.
GPC	gel permeation chromatography.
HEETP	height equivalent to an effective theoretical plate.
HETP	height equivalent to a theoretical plate.
HP	Hewlett-Packard.
HPLC	high performance liquid chromatography.
HRGC	high resolution gas chromatography.
ID	column internal diameter.
IRD	infrared detection.
LC	liquid chromatography.
MDC	multidimensional chromatography.
MD-GC	multidimensional gas chromatography.
MIP	microwave-induced plasma.
MSD	mass selective detection.
NPD	nitrogen-phosphorous detector.
PLOT	porous layer open tubular.
PNA	paraffins, olefins and aromatics.

RI	retention index.
SCOT	support coated open tubular.
SFC	supercritical fluid chromatography.
S/N	signal-to-noise.
TCD	thermal conductivity detector.
TLC	thin layer chromatography.
UTE	utilization of the theoretical efficiency.
WCOT	wall coated open tubular.

APPENDIX III. GLOSSARY OF CHROMATOGRAPHIC TERMS

Adsorbent – chromatographic stationary phase used in gas solid adsorption chromatography.

Bleed – the inherent baseline noise level emanating from a column due to decomposition of the stationary phase or release of low molecular weight synthetic by-products trapped within the polymer.

Coating efficiency – an indication of column performance relative to the theoretical ideal, h_{min}. Also termed the percent coating efficiency or utilization of theoretical efficiency (UTE).

Cross-linked – polymerization of the stationary phase allowing immobilization of the phase for improved column lifetime and durability.

Dead time, t_m – the time that the components spend in the mobile phase measured by the retention time of an unretained component. Also referred to as the "hold-up" time.

Distribution Constant, K_D – equilibrium constant describing the partitioning of the component between the two phases in a chromatographic system.

Efficiency – expression of the broadening of the sample plug as it travels the length of the column.

Film thickness, d_f – the thickness of the stationary phase coating.

Fused silica – synthetic glass used as a column tubing material. Fused silica is superior to other glasses because of its inherent strength, flexibility and inert surface.

HETP, h – height equivalent to a theoretical plate. Measure of column efficiency.

McReynolds constants – a system for classifying stationary phases in terms of their selectivity relative to squalane.

Mobile phase – the phase in a chromatographic system which is in motion relative to the other. In capillary gas chromatography the mobile phase is the carrier gas.

Overload – a saturation of the stationary phase by a component of the sample causing distortion of the peak shape.

Partition ratio, k – a measure of the partitioning of the sample component between the stationary and mobile phases. Also termed the capacity ratio.

Phase ratio, β – the column volume occupied by the mobile phase relative to that volume occupied by the stationary phase.

PLOT (porous layer open tubular) – column used for capillary gas-solid adsorption chromatography made by depositing a layer of adsorbent material on the internal wall of the tubing.

Polyimide – material used as a protective outer coating for fused silica capillary columns.

Resolution, R – the ability of the chromatographic system to separate the "critical pair."

Retention index (Kovats'), I_a^s – a system to measure the retention of compound, a, on a given stationary phase, s, expressed as a hypothetical n-alkane.

Retention time, t_R – the time for a sample component to elute from a chromatographic column measured at the peak maximum.

Selectivity – physicochemical interactions between the component and the chromatographic system. In capillary gas chromatography, selectivity is determined by the nature of the stationary phase.

Selectivity factor, α – relative retention time of a component pair commonly used to express the selectivity of the stationary phase.

Stationary phase – in gas chromatography, the phase which determines the selective interactions between the sample components and the chromatographic system. The stationary phase can be either a polymer liquid or solid adsorbent material.

Tailing – skew in the downside shape of the peak which indicates nonideal partitioning.

Theoretical plate, n – a measure of chromatographic efficiency commonly used in high resolution chromatography to express column performance.

Trennzahl (or Separation Number), TZ – measure of efficiency expressed as the resolution between two consecutive homologs.

WCOT (wall coated open tubular) – capillary column used for gas-liquid partition chromatography in which the stationary liquid phase is coated as a uniform layer on the internal wall of the tubing.

xx

INDEX